One Hundred

BIBLE STORIES

Activity Book

913

CPH®

SAINT LOUIS

Project Editor: Kenneth C. Wagener

Unless otherwise noted, Scripture quotations are taken from the HOLY BIBLE, NEW INTERNATIONAL VERSION®. NIV®. Copyright © 1973, 1978, 1984 by the International Bible Society. Used by permission of Zondervan Publishing House. All rights reserved.

Copyright © 1998 Concordia Publishing House
3558 S. Jefferson Avenue, St.Louis, MO 63118-3968
Manufactured in the United States of America

4   5   6   7   8   9   10   05   06   05   04   03   02   01   00   99

Contents

The Undivided Kingdom (about 1100 to 975 B.C.)

The Divided Kingdom (about 975 to 588 B.C.)

The New Testament

The Youth of Jesus (about 7 B.C. to A.D. 6)

The Public Ministry of Christ (about A.D. 29 to 33)

The Parables of the Savior (about A.D. 29 to 33)

The Passion and Death of Christ (about A.D. 33)

The Glorified Christ (about A.D. 33)

The Church of Christ (about A.D. 33 to 60)

Preface

For the past 50 years, *One Hundred Bible Stories* has introduced students and families to the truth and beauty of God's Word. Through the actual words of Holy Scripture and distinctive artwork, the history of God and His people comes alive on every page, drawing us into the story of God's grace revealed in Jesus Christ.

With the release of the new, revised edition of *One Hundred Bible Stories*, Concordia Publishing House is pleased to present the accompanying *One Hundred Bible Stories Activity Book*, a revision of *Working with God's Word*.

One Hundred Bible Stories Activity Book is ideal for day school and Sunday school classrooms, for confirmation and midweek programs, for home schooling, and for family devotions. Each session poses engaging, relevant questions for classroom discussion and individual reflection. As with the previous edition, the activities have been written for persons ages 9 and above. Parents and teachers will welcome the ways that the two sections, "Thinking about God's Word" and "Working with God's Word," draw students into the biblical story. In a world characterized by busy schedules and little time for reading and reflecting on God's Word, *One Hundred Bible Stories Activity Book* offers an interesting study and regular review of key narratives in Holy Scripture.

"Nuggets from the inexhaustible gold mine of the Scriptures." These words from the original Foreword still describe *One Hundred Bible Stories*. We pray that God will bless you as you read and study His Word, and that He will fulfill His purpose to use the Holy Scriptures to "make you wise for salvation through faith in Christ Jesus" (2 Timothy 3:15).

1

The Creation: The First to the Fourth Day
(Genesis 1)

Thinking about God's Word

1. What word tells who created the world?
2. What is meant by "the beginning"?
3. Who lived before the beginning?
4. Which words tell what happened every time God said, "Let there be"?
5. In what way does God continue to create the world today?
6. How was it possible for God to create all things out of nothing?
7. In John 1:1–3, the Son of God is called "the Word." What connection is there between "the Word" and "God said"? Which persons of the Holy Trinity were active in the work of creation?

Working with God's Word

On the blank lines write on which day God created the following.

1. moon _____
2. night _____
3. earth _____
4. trees _____
5. sky _____
6. sun _____
7. day _____
8. waters _____
9. stars _____
10. planets _____
11. ocean _____
12. rivers _____

Fill in the blanks.

1. In the beginning God _____ the heavens and the earth.

2. The earth was _____ and empty.

3. God separated the light from the _____.

4. God called the light _____.

5. The darkness God called _____.

6. God called the expanse _____.

7. God called the dry ground _____.

8. Each day consisted of evening and _____.

9

2

The Creation: The Fifth to the Seventh Day
(Genesis 1)

Thinking about God's Word

1. How can you tell that the Creator made a large number of living creatures in the beginning?
2. Which words show that God wanted the whole earth to be filled with living things?
3. Who is meant by "Us" and "Our" when God spoke about making people?
4. How many human beings did God make on the sixth day? Which words show that God wanted them to have children who in time would live all over the world?
5. In what two ways did God say that people were to be rulers over the other creatures?
6. What was the chief difference between people and the other moving creatures?
7. Which words tell that there was not a mistake or a flaw in anything God had made?
8. How did God show on the seventh day that there was nothing more that He wanted to create?
9. Did God let the animals look out for themselves after He had created them? How does He still preserve and govern them?
10. How does the picture try to show that there was peace and happiness among God's creatures?
11. Tell what God created on each day. Think of the wise plan God followed in what He made from day to day.

Working with God's Word

On the blank lines write on which day God created the following:

1. man _____
2. robins _____
3. cats _____
4. turtles _____
5. deer _____
6. sharks _____
7. cows _____
8. whales _____
9. worms _____
10. chickens _____
11. frogs _____
12. bears _____
13. woman _____
14. mice _____
15. eagles _____
16. dogs _____
17. fish _____
18. ants _____

Fill in the blanks.

1. God said, "Let birds fly above the _____ across the expanse of the sky."

2. God blessed them and said, "Be fruitful and _____ in number."

3. Birds and water animals were made on the _____ day.

4. God said, "Let Us make man in Our _____, in Our likeness."

5. So God created man in His own _____.

6. Male and _____ He created them.

7. God told them, "Fill the earth and _____ it."

8. On the sixth day God created animals and _____.

9. Everything that God made was very _____.

10. God _____ the seventh day and made it holy.

3

Adam and Eve in Paradise
(Genesis 2)

Thinking about God's Word

1. What was the difference between the way God made people and the way He made the other creatures?
2. How did God make woman? Did she also have the image of God?
3. What reason did God give for making woman?
4. What place did God prepare as a home for the first married couple?
5. God revealed His glory and majesty in His great work of creation. How did He show His power? His wisdom? His goodness?
6. Why does God have a right to be adored by all creatures? Why has He a right to give them commandments? Why is it their duty to obey Him only?
7. Has anything been invented by people that is as marvelous as your reason or your memory?
8. What is another name for Eden?

Working with God's Word

Fill in the blanks.

1. God formed man from the _____ of the ground.
2. God breathed into man's nostrils the _____ of life.
3. Then man became a living _____.
4. God planted a garden in _____.
5. The tree of life stood in the _____ of the garden.
6. God put Adam into the Garden of _____ to work it.
7. God said, "It is not good for the man to be _____."
8. God said, "I will make a _____ suitable for him."
9. The woman was made out of one of Adam's _____.
10. The man said, "She shall be called _____, for she was taken out of man."

True or False

1. God formed woman of the dust of the ground.   T   F
2. The Lord God planted a garden in Eden.   T   F
3. The Lord made every tree to bear good food.   T   F
4. God put man into the garden to take care of it.   T   F
5. There were two trees from which the man and woman should not eat.   T   F
6. The Lord God did not want the man to be alone.   T   F
7. The Lord made a wife for Adam.   T   F
8. Adam called the new human being "woman."   T   F
9. Adam planted a garden in Eden.   T   F
10. Adam and Eve were holy.   T   F

4

The Fall into Sin

(Genesis 3)

Thinking about God's Word

1. How did God communicate with Adam and Eve?
2. What special command had God given them?
3. How were they to show their obedience and love toward God?
4. Did they have the ability to fulfill God's command?
5. Tell how the first two people became disobedient.
6. Could Adam and Eve really hide from God?
7. What came into the world as a result of Adam and Eve's disobedience?
8. Whose fault is it that we are sinners?
9. Name four evils that have come into the world because of sin.

Working with God's Word

Answer the following questions.

1. Who tempted the woman through the serpent? _____

2. Who tempted the man?

   _____

3. Who said they were not to eat of the tree of the knowledge of good and evil?

   _____

4. What would happen if they did eat?

   _____

5. Who said they would not die?

   _____

6. Who spoke the first lie in the world?

   _____

7. How did the fruit look to the woman?

   _____

8. What sin did the man and the woman commit? _____

9. Why did they try to hide from God?

   _____

10. Where did they think they could hide?

    _____

Circle the answer that makes each sentence correct.

1. A serpent is a (servant—snake—eel).
2. This lesson is taken from the Bible in the book of (Exodus—Numbers—Genesis).
3. Crafty means (hard—brave—sly—wise).
4. The serpent spoke first to the (man—woman—snake—tree).
5. The forbidden tree was the tree of (life—knowledge).
6. The devil tried to make the woman (curious—proud—afraid).
7. Adam took the fruit from the (serpent—woman—tree—devil).
8. Adam and Eve hid themselves (by a river—in the bushes— among the trees—in the grass).
9. (God—Man and woman—Animals) brought sin into the world.

5

The Promise of the Savior
(Genesis 3)

Thinking about God's Word

1. What was the complete punishment the man and the woman deserved because of their sin?

2. What sentence did God pronounce on the woman? on the man?

3. How was the serpent punished?

4. Whom did Eve blame for her sin? Whom did Adam blame for his sin?

5. Why did God clothe Adam and Eve after they had sinned?

6. Why did God not let them eat of the tree of life?

7. What are the most terrible consequences of sin? You will find the answer in Romans 6:23.

8. How did you become a sinner?

9. What are some of the things Adam left behind when he lost Paradise?

10. Look forward with Adam. Why could he still have hope in God's beautiful world?

11. Look upward with Adam. What did he believe? What do you believe?

Working with God's Word

Answer the questions with one word.

1. Whom did the Lord God call?

   _____

2. How did Adam say he felt toward God?

   _____

3. Whom did the man blame for his sin?

   _____

4. Whom did the woman blame for her sin? _____

5. Whom did the Lord God punish first?

   _____

6. Who would crush the head of the devil? _____

7. Who was to bring forth children in sorrow? _____

8. For whose sake was the ground cursed? _____

9. Who made clothes for Adam and his wife? _____

10. Who guarded the way to the tree of life? _____

Draw a line under the correct answer to each question.

1. Whom did Adam blame for having led him to eat of the fruit?
   (devil—serpent—himself—God—woman)

2. Whom did the woman blame for leading her into sin?
   (serpent—Adam—God—herself)

3. Whose fault was it that Adam sinned?
   (devil's—Eve's—God's—Adam's)

4. Whose fault was it that Eve sinned?
   (devil's—serpent's—God's—Eve's)

5. Who drove Adam and his wife from the garden?
   (devil—cherubim—God—wild animals)

6. Why did Adam and his wife try to hide from God?
   (They were naked—They were as gods—They had sinned)

7. How did God punish Adam, his wife, and the serpent?
   (He killed them—He scolded them—He cursed them)

8. Who are sinners?
   (only heathen—all except Christians—only grown people—all people)

9. For whose sake did God curse the ground?
   (His sake—the woman's—Adam's—Satan's)

6 Cain and Abel
(Genesis 4)

Thinking about God's Word

1. What is a way that Cain and Abel worshiped God?
2. How did Cain first show his anger after God did not respect his offering?
3. Answer this question correctly for Cain and give a reason for your answer: "Am I my brother's keeper?"
4. Was the mark that God set on Cain a blessing or a punishment? Why?

Working with God's Word

Answer each question with one word.

1. What name did Adam give his wife? _____

2. Who was Eve's first child? _____

3. Who was Eve's second child? _____

4. What did Cain bring as an offering to God? _____

5. What did Abel bring? _____

6. With whose offering was the Lord pleased? _____

7. Why was Cain cursed? _____

8. Who cursed Cain? _____

9. What would no longer yield its crops for Cain? _____

10. How did the Lord protect Cain from being killed? _____

Draw a line under the word that makes each sentence true.

1. The name Eve means (evil—ever—mother—woman).

2. Killing is forbidden in the (Third—Fourth—Fifth—Sixth) Commandment.

3. Abel was a (farmer—carpenter—mason—shepherd).

4. Cain was a (farmer—carpenter—mason—shepherd).

5. God cursed Cain and made him a (foreigner—wanderer—beggar—sinner).

6. This Bible lesson is written in the book of (Exodus—Numbers—Genesis—John).

7. God put a (blot—sore—mark—sickness) upon Cain.

8. Cain was (older—younger) than his brother.

9. Adam was the (brother—mother—father—uncle) of Cain and Abel.

10. Cain (could—could not) have had his sin forgiven.

16

7

From Adam to Noah

(Genesis 5)

Thinking about God's Word

1. Which words tell that Adam's children did not have the image of God as Adam had it before the Fall?
2. When Adam died, which words of the Lord came true? See Lesson 5.
3. The time of each firstborn son is called a generation. How many generations were there from Adam to Noah?
4. What does it mean that "men began to call on the name of the LORD"?
5. Which words tell us that Enoch loved God?
6. How did God show in the case of Enoch that He would give eternal life to those who believed in the promised Savior?

Working with God's Word

Answer each question with one word or number.

1. How old was Adam when Seth was born? _____

2. How old did Adam live to be?

   _____

3. Who was Seth's first son?

   _____

4. On whose name did men begin to call?

   _____

5. How old did Enoch live to be?

   _____

6. Who was the oldest man who lived from Adam to Noah? _____

7. Whom did the Lord take to heaven without letting him die?

   _____

8. Who was Noah's father?

   _____

9. How long did Noah's father live?

   _____

10. How many sons did Noah have?

    _____

Draw a line under the correct answer to each question.

1. Who was the oldest man in the world? (Adam—Jared—Methuselah—Seth)

2. What was the age of the oldest man in the world? (905—969—912—996)

3. Who was Adam's son? (Enos—Jared—Methuselah—Seth)

4. Who went to heaven alive? (Enos—Enoch—Adam—Seth)

5. How old did Adam get to be? (969—912—930—962)

6. How many years did Adam live after Seth was born? (600—700—800—900)

7. In whose time did men begin to call upon the name of the Lord? (Lamech's—Adam's—Seth's—Jared's)

8. Who was Noah's son? (Enos—Enoch—Shem—Lamech)

9. Why did these early Bible people get so old? (They were healthy—They had good doctors—They never worked too hard—God wanted them to teach others)

8
The Flood
(Genesis 6–9)

Thinking about God's Word

1. What did the Lord see when men increased in number?
2. What did the Lord plan to do?
3. How was Noah different from the other people?
4. What did God tell Noah?
5. How do the words "Noah did everything just as God commanded him" show that Noah believed God?
6. Which people were saved by the ark?
7. Why can God not take pleasure in wickedness nor let evil dwell with Him?
8. Which blessing that God first gave to Adam and Eve did He now give again to Noah and his family?

Working with God's Word

Answer each question with one word or number.

1. What happened to people as they began to increase in number?
   _____
2. What did the Lord say He would do with people? _____
3. Who found favor in the eyes of the Lord? _____ .
4. What did the Lord tell Noah to build?
   _____
5. What was the Lord going to destroy?
   _____
6. How many days and nights did it rain?
   _____

7. How many days did the water stay on earth? _____
8. On which mountain did the ark rest?
   _____
9. What did Noah do after he left the ark? _____
10. What did the Lord place in the sky as a sign that He would not send another flood to destroy the whole earth?
    _____

Answer each question.

1. Did God send a flood to destroy the world because the people were wicked?
   Yes   No
2. Did it rain for 50 days and 50 nights?
   Yes   No
3. Were the mountains covered with water?
   Yes   No
4. Did the water remain on the earth 200 days?   Yes   No
5. Did the ark come to rest on Ararat?
   Yes   No
6. Were all people and all animals destroyed by the flood?
   Yes   No
7. Did God use the rainbow as a sign?
   Yes   No
8. Does God punish wickedness today?
   Yes   No

9

The Tower of Babel

(Genesis 11)

Thinking about God's Word

1. What did people decide to do instead of spreading out over the earth?
2. What sins did the people commit by saying:
   a. "Come, let us build ourselves a city"?
   b. "Let us build ourselves a tower that reaches to the heavens"?
   c. Let us "make a name for ourselves"?
3. How and why did God confuse the people?
4. How did the changing of languages keep the people from building their city and tower?
5. How did the people of Babel transgress God's commandments? What was their punishment?

Working with God's Word

Fill in the blanks.

1. The whole _____ had one language.
2. Men moved _____.
3. They found a plain; and they _____ there.
4. The people said to each other, "Let us build ourselves a _____ with a tower."
5. They said, "Let us make a _____ for ourselves."
6. God said, "Let Us go down and confuse their _____."
7. So the Lord _____ them.

8. This lesson was taken from the book of _____.

Fill in the blanks with words from below.

1. All the people spoke one _____.
2. These people found a _____ where they wished to stay.
3. They wanted to build a city and a _____.
4. They wanted to make a _____ for themselves.
5. The _____ was displeased with the people.
6. The Lord punished the people by changing their _____.
7. The Lord scattered them over the face of the _____.
8. The people of Babel were _____.

earth

language

plain

tower

proud

name

Lord

10

The Call of Abram
(Genesis 12)

Thinking about God's Word

1. What command came to Abram, whom God later named Abraham, from the Lord?
2. Where did God want Abraham to go? What did Abraham have to leave behind?
3. What threefold promise did God give with His command?
4. Which of these promises meant the same as the promise given to Adam and Eve after the Fall?
5. Which words show that Abraham believed God and did what He said?
6. How did Abraham worship God in public after he arrived in Canaan?
7. How did the Lord answer him when Abraham said that he was still childless?
8. Why did it take great faith on Abraham's part to believe this promise?
9. What does it mean to have faith in God?

Working with God's Word

Answer each question.

1. Who called Abraham out of his home-land? _____

2. Which persons went with Abraham?

   _____

3. Near which city did Lot pitch his tent?

   _____

4. What promise did God make to Abraham one night?

   _____

5. How old was Abraham when God came to him another time?

   _____

6. Who gave Abraham faith?

   _____

7. How did God call you and give you faith? _____

Answer each question with one word from below.

1. Who was Abraham's nephew?

   _____

2. Which word tells that Abraham had no child? _____

3. Which word means family?

   _____

4. Which city was filled with wicked men and sinners? _____

5. Which word tells that Abraham had faith? _____

6. What did Abraham build to the Lord?

   _____

7. What is the meaning of offspring?

   _____

household	Shem
Sodom	believed
eighth day	children
childless	Lot
altar	Jordan

11 The Promise of Isaac

(Genesis 18)

Thinking about God's Word

1. In what form did the Lord come to Abraham at the time of this story?
2. For what special purpose had the Lord come to Abraham?
3. How did Sarah hear the Lord's promise, even though it was not spoken directly to her?
4. How would you answer the question, "Why did Sarah laugh?"
5. Name a promise God makes to us that has not as yet been fulfilled in us. Do you believe it will be fulfilled? Give a reason.

Working with God's Word

Answer each question.

1. Who were the three men who came to Abraham's tent? _____
2. How did Abraham show kindness toward them? _____
   _____
3. Which words show that the men accepted Abraham's invitation?
   _____
4. What foods did they have for their meal?
   _____
5. What promise did the Lord give Abraham? _____
   _____
6. How can you tell that Sarah did not believe the promise? _____
   _____

7. Why could Sarah hardly believe that she would have a son?
   _____
8. How did the Lord know that Sarah laughed? _____
9. Why did Sarah deny that she had laughed? _____

Fill in each blank with a word from below.

1. Abraham and Sarah lived in a _____.
2. Three men _____ Abraham.
3. These men were the _____ and two angels.
4. Abraham _____ to meet the men.
5. Sarah used flour to make _____.
6. A servant prepared a _____.
7. The Lord said, "Sarah, your wife will have a _____."
8. Sarah _____ to herself.
9. Sarah told a _____.
10. Nothing is too _____ for the Lord.

ran	tent	Lord
son	hard	bread
laughed	lie	calf
visited		

21

Sodom and Gomorrah

(Genesis 19)

Thinking about God's Word

1. Where was Lot sitting when the angels came to him?
2. Where did Lot take the angels?
3. Which words show that Lot tried to turn the men of Sodom from their evil ways?
4. What did the angels do to the wicked men?
5. Why had the angels come to visit Lot?
6. Whom did the angels try to save besides Lot and his wife and daughters? Why were they not saved?
7. What was destroyed? Who were destroyed?
8. Whom did Lot's wife disobey when she looked back? How was she punished?
9. Why were the people of Sodom and Gomorrah destroyed? See Genesis 18:20–32 and 2 Peter 2:6.

Working with God's Word

Answer each question.

1. How did Lot show kindness to the two angels? _____

2. What did the men of Sodom want with the angels? _____

3. How did the angels show their mighty power? _____

4. Why had the angels come to Lot's home? _____

5. Whom did Lot try to save from death?
_____

6. At what time of the day did Lot and his family leave the city?

_____

7. What warning did the angels give to Lot and his family?

_____

8. How did the Lord destroy the two cities? _____

9. Who looked behind her against the angels' command? _____

10. How was she punished?

_____

Circle the answer that makes each sentence true.

1. (Two—Three—Four—Five) angels came to visit Lot.

2. Lot was sitting in the gate of (Sodom —Gomorrah—Sodom and Gomorrah).

3. The men of Sodom who came to Lot's house were (young—old—young and old).

4. Lot called the men of the city (sinners —friends—sons-in-law—heathen).

5. The angels struck the men with (brimstone—blindness—fire—a rod).

6. Lot's sons-in-law had no (time— belief—courage—love).

7. The two cities were burned at (morning—evening—noon-midnight).

8. (Three—Four—Five—Six) people of Sodom were saved.

13

The Offering of Isaac
(Genesis 22)

Thinking about God's Word

1. What did Abraham name his son?
2. How did God test Abraham?
3. Why must God's command have been a shock to Abraham? What did Abraham's faith in God move him to do just the same?
4. How did Abraham's answer to Isaac again prove his strong faith in God? How did God fulfill what Abraham said and believed a short time later? What Lamb did God Himself provide as an offering about 2,000 years later?
5. In which words did the Angel of the Lord tell Abraham that he had passed the test?
6. What did the Angel of the Lord say Abraham's blessing would be?
7. Name three ways in which Abraham's son and God's Son were the same.
8. God spared Abraham's son, but what did He do with His own?

Working with God's Word

Answer each question.

1. To which area did God tell Abraham to take Isaac? _____
2. Why were fire, knife, and wood taken on the journey?_____
3. How did Abraham answer Isaac's question? _____
4. How did Abraham show that he really meant to carry out God's command?

_____

5. Who saved Isaac from death?

_____

6. What did the Angel of the Lord say to Abraham when they talked the second time? _____
7. How can you tell that Abraham had a strong faith? _____
8. How many children did God promise Abraham? _____
9. In whom shall all the nations of the earth be blessed? _____

Draw a circle around the Yes or No answer.

1. Did God tell Abraham to take his son to the land of Moriah?   Yes   No
2. Did it take four days before they saw the place in the distance?   Yes   No
3. Did the servants carry the wood up Mt. Nebo?   Yes   No
4. Did Isaac carry the wood up the mountain?   Yes   No
5. Did Abraham kill his son?   Yes   No
6. Is the Angel of the Lord the same as Jesus?   Yes   No
7. Is a ram a male sheep?   Yes   No
8. Did Abraham love God more than he loved Isaac?   Yes   No

14

Isaac and His Family

(Genesis 27)

Thinking about God's Word

1. Who was Isaac's oldest son?
2. How can you tell that Isaac intended to give the blessing to Esau?
3. How did Rebekah try to stop that?
4. How did Jacob lie to his father?

Working with God's Word

Answer each question.

1. How old was Isaac when he got married? _____

2. Who became his wife? _____

3. Who were Isaac's two sons?

   _____

4. To whom did Isaac wish to give the blessing? _____

5. How did Rebekah make Jacob's skin feel like Esau's? _____

6. From which animals did Rebekah make tasty food? _____

7. Who got the blessing? _____

8. Why was it easy to fool Isaac?

   _____

9. Which blessing did Isaac give to Jacob?

   _____

On the blank lines write the word from below that answers the question.

1. Who was Esau's brother?

   _____

2. Who was Isaac's wife?

   _____

3. What did Isaac want Esau to get for him? _____

4. How many goats did Rebekah use to get meat ready for Isaac?

   _____

5. When Jacob came into his father's room, who did he say he was?

   _____

6. Whose voice did Isaac think he heard when Jacob was in the room?

   _____

7. Whose hands did Isaac think he felt when Jacob was in the room?

   _____

8. What did Jacob have to tell to get the blessing? _____

Esau	food
Rebekah	Esau's
Jacob	lies
two	Jacob's
Abraham	three

15

Jacob's Stairway
(Genesis 28)

Thinking about God's Word

1. Where had Esau been while Jacob was receiving the blessing from his father?
2. Why did Esau weep? What blessing did Isaac give him?
3. Which words of his blessing do you think led Esau to hate his brother and want to kill him?
4. How did God appear to Jacob after he fled?
5. In which words did the Lord give Jacob a blessing?
6. What three names did Jacob give to the place where he had his dream?
7. What vow did Jacob make before he left Bethel?
8. Have you ever been blessed by someone? When? Where? How? Why?

Working with God's Word

Answer each question.

1. What did Esau say when his father asked his name? _____
2. How did Esau show that he wanted a blessing, too? _____
3. Which part of Esau's blessing made him Jacob's servant? _____
4. What did Esau intend to do to his brother? _____
5. To what place did Rebekah tell Jacob to flee? _____

6. Who stood at the top of the stairway in Jacob's dream? _____
7. What name did Jacob give to the place where he dreamed? _____
8. What were the two main parts of Jacob's vow to God for His protection?

_____

Answer these questions with names from below.

1. Who said, "Bless me, too, my father"?
_____
2. Who said, "I will give you and your descendants the land on which you are lying"? _____
3. Who said, "May God Almighty bless you"? _____
4. Who said, "You will live by the sword"?
_____
5. Who said, "This is none other than the house of God"? _____
6. Who said, "Who are you"?
_____
7. Who said, "This is the gate of heaven"?
_____
8. Who said, "I am your son, your first-born"? _____
9. Who said, "Flee at once to my brother Laban"? _____

God	Rebekah
Jacob	Esau
Isaac	Laban

16

Jacob's Family

(Genesis 37)

Thinking about God's Word

1. How many wives did Jacob have?
2. How many years did Jacob stay in Haran? Which words show that God gave him many gifts while he was there?
3. Which words show that God wanted Jacob to return to Canaan?
4. Why did Jacob not have to fear the long journey back to Canaan with his family?
5. Do you think Jacob made a mistake in his love for his sons? Why or why not?
6. Which words tell how Joseph's brothers felt towards him?
7. Which words show that the brothers and the father understood the meaning of Joseph's dreams?

Working with God's Word

Answer each question.

1. For whom did Jacob serve Laban 14 years? _____

2. How many years did Jacob work to earn cattle for himself? _____

3. Why did Jacob return to Canaan with his family? _____

4. How many sons did Jacob have?

   _____

5. Who was Jacob's best-loved son?

   _____

6. How did Jacob show his great love for Joseph? _____

7. How many dreams did Joseph have?

   _____

8. What did the dreams mean? _____

9. Who sent the dreams? _____

10. What were the names of Jacob's sons?

Draw a circle around Yes or No.

1. Did Joseph have 12 brothers?
   Yes   No

2. Did Joseph feed the flock with his brothers?
   Yes   No

3. Was Joseph a shepherd?
   Yes   No

4. Did Jacob love Joseph more than Benjamin?
   Yes   No

5. Did Joseph make a beautiful robe?
   Yes   No

6. Did Jacob say, "You shall indeed reign over us"?
   Yes   No

7. Did Jacob scold Joseph for his dreams?
   Yes   No

17

Joseph and His Brothers

(Genesis 37)

Thinking about God's Word

1. How can you tell that Joseph did not go with his brothers when they went to Shechem?
2. How do the words of Israel to Joseph show that he wanted to be a God-pleasing father?
3. What name did the brothers call Joseph? Explain why "name-calling" is a sin against the Fifth Commandment.
4. What did the brothers plan to do when they saw Joseph coming toward them?
5. What did the brothers do after they threw Joseph into a cistern? How did this show their hard-heartedness?
6. How did the brothers deceive their father?
7. Show how from this lesson the brothers hurt Joseph, Jacob, and most of all themselves. Which words of Jacob tell how deeply he was hurt?
8. How were Jesus and Joseph alike? How were they not alike?

Thinking about God's Word

Answer each question.

1. Where did Jacob's sons go to feed the flocks? _____

2. Whom did Jacob send to see how the brothers were doing? _____

3. What did the brothers say when they saw Joseph in the distance? _____

4. Who suggested that Joseph be thrown into a cistern? _____

5. Which brother suggested selling Joseph?

_____

6. Who bought Joseph from the brothers?

_____

7. How many shekels of silver were paid for Joseph? _____

8. What two lies did the brothers want their father to believe? _____

9. How did Jacob show that he believed the brother's lie? _____

Fill in the blank spaces with words from below.

1. The brothers fed their father's flock near _____.
2. Israel said to Joseph, "Go and see if all is well with your _____."
3. The brothers said, "Let's _____ him."
4. _____ tried to rescue Joseph out of their hand.
5. They _____ Joseph of his robe.
6. _____ said, "Come, let's sell our brother."
7. They sold him to the _____.
8. Reuben _____ his clothes when he saw the cistern empty.
9. Jacob said, "Some ferocious animal has _____ him."
10. Jacob refused to be _____.

Reuben	comforted	tore
Shechem	stripped	Ishmaelites
brothers	Judah	kill
devoured		

27

18

Joseph Serves Pharaoh

(Genesis 41)

Thinking about God's Word

1. Why did Pharaoh have to find someone in place of his magicians to interpret his dreams?
2. How did Pharaoh know that Joseph could interpret dreams? (See Genesis 41:9–13.)
3. How did Joseph show his humility as he stood before Pharaoh?
4. In which words did Joseph give all honor and glory to God?
5. What advice did Joseph give Pharaoh together with the interpretation?
6. How did Joseph rise from slave and prisoner to ruler of Egypt? Find your answer in Joseph's own words.

Working with God's Word

Answer each question with one word.

1. Who had dreams in this lesson?

   _____

2. How many cows did Pharaoh see coming from the water? _____

3. What kind of grain grew on the stalks Pharaoh saw in his dream?

   _____

4. Whom did Pharaoh first ask to interpret his dreams? _____

5. According to Joseph, who alone could answer Pharaoh's dreams?

   _____

6. How many years of plenty and famine would there be? _____

7. Whom did Pharaoh choose as one discerning and wise? _____

8. Throughout which land did Joseph travel? _____

9. What did he collect? _____

Underline the word that makes each sentence true.

1. Pharaoh had (1—2—3—4) dreams.

2. Pharaoh was the (king—captain—president—prince) of Egypt.

3. Pharaoh's dreams told about (14—7—10—16) years of famine.

4. Joseph said that (he—magicians—Jacob—God) would answer Pharaoh.

5. Pharoah put Joseph in charge of (Egypt—Israel—food—people).

6. Joseph gathered (one-fifth—one-half—all—one-sixth) of the crops during the seven years of plenty.

19

The Journeys of Joseph's Brothers
(Genesis 42–43)

Thinking about God's Word

1. How can you tell that there was a famine also in Canaan during the lean years?
2. What news had Jacob received from Egypt?
3. How did Joseph treat the brothers when they came to him?
4. According to the words of Jacob, who alone could grant mercy?
5. Why did Joseph weep?
6. How can you tell that Joseph still remembered all of his brothers?
7. Why do you suppose Joseph gave Benjamin a greater portion of goods than the others?
8. How could Joseph easily have taken revenge on his brothers for having sold him? Why didn't he?

Working with God's Word

Answer each question.

1. Where was there plenty of grain?

   _____

2. Why did Jacob need grain from Egypt?

   _____

3. Whom did Jacob send to get the grain?

   _____

4. Which brother did Joseph want to see?

   _____

5. Whom did Joseph order bound?

   _____

6. Why did the father not want Benjamin to go to Egypt?

   _____

7. What would happen to Jacob if something happened to Benjamin?

   _____

Fill in the blank spaces with words from below.

1. Behold, there was grain in _____.

2. Ten of Joseph's _____ went to buy grain.

3. They _____ down to Joseph.

4. Joseph turned away from them and began to _____.

5. Joseph gave orders to get _____ for his brothers.

6. Joseph's brothers _____ with him.

ate	Egypt	brothers	bowed
grain	weep	true	guilty

29

1. Where did Jacob ask his sons to go again a second time?

   _____

2. When did Joseph want his brothers to eat with him? _____

3. How did Joseph show that he loved Benjamin? _____

4. Who got five measures of food?

   _____

5. What did Joseph command to be put into Benjamin's sack beside the grain?

   _____

Circle Yes or No.

1. Did Jacob say, "I have heard that there is grain in Egypt"?
   Yes   No

2. Did Joseph's brothers recognize him?
   Yes   No

3. Were Joseph's brothers invited for supper?
   Yes   No

4. Did Simeon eat with the brothers?
   Yes   No

5. Was Jacob still alive at this time?
   Yes   No

6. Did Benjamin get four times as much as his brothers?
   Yes   No

7. Was Reuben's name mentioned in this lesson?
   Yes   No

20

Joseph Makes Himself Known to His Brothers
(Genesis 44–45)

Thinking about God's Word

1. Of what did the steward accuse the brothers?
2. How can you tell from the answer of the brothers that they were sure none of them had done the wrong?
3. Why did the brothers all return to the city when the guilty one was found?
4. Whom only did Joseph say he wanted to keep as a servant? Why?
5. How did the words of Judah show that his heart was changed?
6. How can you tell that this is what Joseph had hoped for in testing his brothers?
7. Why were the brothers afraid at first?
8. What did Joseph say and do to show his brothers that he forgave them?
9. Which words show that Joseph honored God as much now as he did when he was in trouble?
10. Why did Joseph forgive his brothers? Read Colossians 3:13.

Working with God's Word

Answer each question.

1. What did Joseph command his steward to do? _____

2. What did the brothers want done to the one who had the cup?

   _____

3. How did the brothers show sorrow and repentance? _____

4. How did Judah keep his promise to Jacob? _____

5. What did Joseph tell the brothers after he heard Judah? _____

6. Why were the brothers afraid of Joseph? _____

7. What did Joseph say to prove that he still trusted God? _____

8. How did Joseph want to take care of his father and brothers? _____

Draw a line under the correct answer to each question.

1. Who followed after the brothers when they left the city? (Joseph—the ruler of the house—a steward—a guard)
2. Who had taken the cup from Joseph? (Benjamin—Judah—Reuben—no one)
3. Who made himself known? (Jacob—Joseph—the brothers—Benjamin)
4. Who wanted to take Benjamin's place and become a slave? (Reuben—Simeon—Judah)
5. What did Judah call Joseph? (king—brother—lord—ruler)
6. Whom did Joseph kiss? (only Benjamin—only Reuben—only Simeon—all the brothers)
7. How did Joseph show that he was a true child of God? (He wept—He nourished—He forgave—He supplied)
8. Which of the brothers was dearest to Joseph's heart? (Benjamin—Reuben—Judah—Simeon)
9. How did Joseph reward evil? (with evil—with good)

31

21

Jacob and Joseph Are Reunited

(Genesis 46–50)

Thinking about God's Word

1. Why did Joseph send carts to Canaan?
2. In his parting words to his brothers, how did Joseph show that he was a good brother?
3. What did Jacob say when he was finally convinced that Joseph was alive?
4. Why was it better for Jacob to go to Egypt to live with Joseph, than for Joseph to go to Canaan to live with Jacob?
5. How can you tell that Jacob was happy and at peace after he saw Joseph?
6. Whom did Jacob bless before he died?
7. Why did the brothers ask Joseph to forgive their trespasses again after their father died? What was Joseph's answer?
8. How did Joseph's answer and his action again show his faith in God and his love for the brothers?
9. Read the first two lines of Romans 8:28. What things seemed evil in Joseph's life? What things seemed good? How did all things work together for good? To whom do all things work together for good?

Working with God's Word

Answer each question with one word.

1. To whom did Joseph give carts and provisions? _____
2. How many shekels of silver did Joseph give to Benjamin? _____
3. To whom did the brothers bring the good news? _____
4. What was Joseph in the land of Egypt? _____

5. What led Jacob to believe Joseph was alive? _____
6. Whom did Jacob send before him to meet Joseph? _____
7. What kind of cart did Joseph use to meet his father? _____
8. Who were afraid after Israel died? _____
9. What did they ask of Joseph? _____
10. Who intended everything for good? _____

Fill in the blank spaces with words from below.

1. Joseph gave each brother new _____.
2. The silver and clothing were signs of Joseph's _____.
3. When Jacob saw Joseph again, he was ready to _____.
4. Joseph went to meet his father in a _____.
5. Joseph settled his _____ and brothers in Egypt.
6. Israel called his sons and _____ them before he died.
7. After Israel had died, the brothers sent word to Joseph and asked him to _____ them.

clothes	forgive	die
father	love	Judah
hate	blessed	chariot
multiplied		

22

The Birth of Moses

(Exodus 1–2)

Thinking about God's Word

1. How did the Lord bless the family of Israel in Egypt? Why didn't the new Pharaoh like this? How did he try to "deal shrewdly with them"?

2. How do you explain the fact that "the more they were oppressed, the more they multiplied"? Of which blessing of God to Abraham are you reminded?

3. Why did Pharaoh want the baby boys drowned?

4. Think of two good reasons why the Levite woman did not drown her son. Why did she not keep him at home longer? Why did she place him by the river?

5. Was it merely by chance that the baby's sister was there when the princess came to bathe? Did the princess know who the girl and her mother were? How were the mother and daughter wise? What did God have to do with their wisdom?

6. Why was the princess not obliged to kill the boy? Why did she keep him?

7. Who became Moses' grandfather by adoption? How did it benefit Moses to live in the palace of the king rather than to live at home with his family? How could it have been harmful?

8. Who gave Moses his name? Exodus 2:10 will tell you what it means.

Working with God's Word

Answer each question.

1. Whom did the king not know about?

   _____

2. How did the king hope to crush the Israelites? _____

3. What very cruel law did he make?

   _____

4. Which mother did not obey this law?

   _____

5. What did she make in which to hide her son? _____

6. What did the mother do with the baby after three months? _____

7. Who came to the river to bathe?

   _____

8. Whom did the baby's sister call as nurse? _____

9. Why did Moses have to flee from Pharaoh? _____

Fill in the blanks with words from below.

1. The new king in Egypt did not know about _____.

2. A _____ woman had a baby boy.

3. Pharaoh ordered, "Every _____ that is born you must throw into the Nile."

4. Moses' mother made him a basket out of _____.

5. The baby's _____ stood at a distance and watched.

6. Pharaoh's daughter saw a _____ among the reeds.

7. The baby's sister asked, "Shall I go and get one of the Hebrew women to _____ the baby for you?"

8. And the _____ went and got the baby's mother.

9. Moses saw an _____ beating a Hebrew.

Joseph	basket
girl	Levite
papyrus	Egyptian
sister	nurse
Moses	Hebrew boy

23

The Call of Moses

(Exodus 3–4)

Thinking about God's Word

1. How did the Lord appear to Moses?
2. Why did the Lord call the Hebrews "My people"? Why did the Lord want to help His people?
3. Which words show that Moses did not think himself great enough to lead God's people out of Egypt?
4. How did God tell Moses that He would help him?
5. What was Moses' second excuse?
6. What power did God give Moses to overcome that excuse?
7. How did the Lord patiently answer the third excuse of Moses?
8. Why did the Lord become angry?
9. How did living in the palace of Pharaoh prepare Moses for this work?
10. Who are the leaders of God's people today? What do we believe about their work?

Working with God's Word

Answer each question with one word.

1. To which mountain did Moses come?
   _____

2. Where did the Angel of the Lord appear to Moses? _____

3. Where were the Lord's people?
   _____

4. To whom did God wish to send Moses?
   _____

5. Who said He would be with Moses?
   _____

6. What did Moses' staff turn into?
   _____

7. Where did Moses put his hand?
   _____

8. What would become of the water poured on dry ground?
   _____

9. Who would speak for Moses?
   _____

Draw a circle around the word or phrase that answers each question.

1. Where did the Angel of the Lord meet Moses? (Carmel—Ararat—Nebo—Horeb)
2. Where were the Lord's people in misery? (Egypt—Canaan—Midian—Sinai)
3. How many excuses did Moses make to God? (1—2—3—4)
4. What turned into a snake? (Moses' hand—Moses' staff—Moses' shoes—Moses' sheep)
5. Where did the Lord tell Moses to put his hand? (in his pocket—over his heart—inside his coat—on the rod)
6. What disease came over Moses' hand? (leprosy—rheumatism—measles—palsy)
7. Where should Moses take water from in Egypt? (river—well—lake—fountain)
8. Who could speak well? (Aaron—Moses—a priest—Pharaoh)
9. Where is this lesson written in the Bible? (Genesis—Exodus—Numbers—Joshua)

24

The Passover

(Exodus 11–12)

Thinking about God's Word

1. How do Moses and Aaron tell Pharaoh that they were sent by God?

2. Whom did Pharoah consider greater than the Lord?

3. Why didn't the miracles have any effect on Pharaoh's heart?

4. List all the directions the Lord told Moses to give His people about the Passover.

5. What would keep death from coming over the firstborn of the children of Israel?

6. How were the children of Israel to remember this day in future generations? What was the feast called?

7. How did the children of Israel show that they believed the Lord?

8. Who is our Passover? How did He become a Passover Lamb for us? See 1 Corinthians 5:7.

Working with God's Word

Fill in the blanks.

1. Moses and _____ talked to Pharaoh.

2. Pharaoh asked, "Who is the _____, that I should obey Him?"

3. The Lord brought nine _____ upon Egypt.

4. The Lord said, "Take a lamb without _____."

5. "And slaughter it at _____."

6. "The blood will be a _____ for you on the houses."

7. "This is a day you are to _____."

8. The Israelites _____ just what the Lord commanded.

Draw a line under the word or phrase that makes each sentence true.

1. (Moses—Aaron—Israel—God) hardened Pharaoh's heart.

2. The Lord brought (8—9—10—11) plagues to Egypt.

3. The Passover lamb was to be (without defect—spotted—white—black).

4. The Passover lamb was to be killed (in the morning—at twilight—at noon—at midnight).

5. The children of Israel were to put blood on the (windows—doors—doorframes—steps) of their homes.

6. The children of Israel were commanded to eat (the best parts—all—as much as they cared for—most) of the Passover lamb.

7. God was going to pass through Egypt (at night—in the morning—in the afternoon—at noon).

8. The Lord was going to strike down all the (firstborn—youngest—girls—boys) in Egypt.

25

The Departure from Egypt

(Exodus 12–14)

Thinking about God's Word

1. Why was there loud wailing in Egypt?
2. When did Pharaoh call Moses and Aaron? Why did the Egyptians now wish the Israelites to leave quickly?
3. Explain why the Lord used a pillar of a cloud during the day and a pillar of fire by night.
4. Why did Pharaoh want the Israelites back?
5. What did Moses say to the people?
6. What miracle did God perform through Moses to enable the people to cross the Red Sea?
7. What do you suppose the Egyptians thought when they rushed into the Red Sea after the children of Israel? How did the Lord finally punish proud Pharaoh and his army in which he trusted?
8. How did the Israelites thank God for His wonderful deliverance? See Exodus 15:1–21.

Working with God's Word

Answer each question.

1. At what time did the Lord strike down all the firstborn of Egypt?

   _____

2. In how many homes was at least one person dead? _____

3. What did Pharaoh say to Moses and Aaron now? _____

4. How many men left Egypt? _____

5. How did the Lord protect His people by day and by night? _____

   _____

6. Where did Pharaoh's army overtake the children of Israel?_____

7. With which words did Moses comfort the frightened people? _____

8. Why were the Israelites able to pass through the Red Sea? _____

9. What happened to Pharaoh and his men? _____

Draw a circle around Yes or No.

1. Did the Angel of Death go through Egypt at noon?   Yes   No
2. Was Pharaoh a firstborn?   Yes   No
3. Was a person dead in every Egyptian house?   Yes   No
4. Did the children of Israel travel on foot?   Yes   No
5. Did the children of Israel have strong faith?   Yes   No
6. Was there a wall of water on both sides of Israel?   Yes   No
7. Did Pharaoh swim to shore?   Yes   No

26

The Giving of the Law

(Exodus 15–16; 19–20)

Thinking about God's Word

1. Why did the Israelites grumble?
2. How did the Lord promise to feed them? How did He keep His promise?
3. How did Moses tell the people to prepare themselves to meet with God?
4. With what signs did God show the people that He had something very serious and important to tell them?
5. Why were the people afraid? What did they say?
6. Where did God take Moses to have him receive the Law?
7. What are the Ten Commandments?

Working with God's Word

Answer each question with a word or two.

1. Who led Israel from the Red Sea?

   _____

2. Where did the children of Israel go after they left the Red Sea?

   _____

3. Who murmured against Moses and Aaron? _____

4. What did the Lord promise Israel for twilight food? _____

5. Which bird did the Lord send for meat? _____

6. What did Israelites call the morning food? _____

7. How long did the children of Israel eat manna? _____

8. Where did Israel camp in the third month? _____

9. How long did Moses stay with God on the mountain? _____

10. What was inscribed by the finger of God? _____

Draw a line under the word that makes each sentence true.

1. Moses led Israel from the (Dead—Red—Caspian—Black) Sea.

2. The children of Israel went into the (forest—desert—water).

3. The Israelites said they were (hungry—thirsty—tired—weak).

4. God sent meat in the (morning—noon—evening—afternoon).

5. God sent manna in the (morning—noon—evening—afternoon).

6. In the (first—second—third—fourth) month the Israelites came to the Desert of Sinai.

7. God wanted the people to meet Him on the (first—second—third—fourth) day.

8. God gave (6—7—8—10) commandments.

9. Moses was on the mountain (30—40—4—50) days and nights.

10. The Ten Commandments are written in Exodus, chapter (10—20—30—40).

The Golden Calf

(Exodus 32; 34)

Thinking about God's Word

1. Why did the children of Israel become impatient with Moses?
2. How did the people worship the idol that Aaron had made? Why was that a sin?
3. What did God say to Moses when He saw the people sin? What had God always called these people before?
4. What did Moses carry with him on the way down from the mount? Whose writing were they?
5. When did Moses get angry? How did he show his anger? What did he make the people do with the idol?
6. With which words did Moses call the people to repentance?
7. How did Moses again get two tables of stone with the Ten Commandments written on them?

Working with God's Word

Answer each question.

1. Whom did the people ask to make gods for them? _____
2. What metal did Aaron use to make the image? _____
3. How did the people worship the idol?

   _____
4. What kind of people did God say the Israelites were? _____

5. Who made the first two tables of stone?_____
6. Who wrote the commandments on the second two tables of stone?

   _____

Fill in the blanks with words from below.

1. _____ asked the people to bring their earrings.
2. The people made _____ offerings to the golden idol.
3. God called the people

   _____.
4. When Moses saw the dancing and the calf, he became _____.
5. _____ broke the tables of stone.
6. Moses ground the golden calf to

   _____.
7. The _____ wrote the Ten Commandments.
8. The people sinned against the _____ Commandment.

Lord	Moses	stiff-necked
burnt	powder	Sinai
Aaron	First	angry
Levi		

28

The Bronze Snake
(Numbers 13–14; 21)

Thinking about God's Word

1. Why did God command Moses to send men into the land before the children of Israel went in?

2. When they returned, what did the explorers report to Moses? Why didn't they think the new land could be taken?

3. What did the Israelites say? How did they again show their lack of trust in God?

4. Who did not agree with the other explorers? In whom did they trust?

5. How long did the Lord say the Israelites would wander?

6. What did the Lord send among the people?

7. How many Israelites did the Lord want to bring into the land of Canaan? Why didn't all of them get there?

8. How was the serpent a type of Christ? Think of these things: lowly, despised, set upon a pole, lifted up, looked upon, lived.

Working with God's Word

Answer each question with one word.

1. Which desert did the children of Israel leave? _____

2. Which land did the Lord want the men to search? _____

3. How long did the explorers stay in the land? _____

4. How did the explorers describe the people of the land? _____

5. Where did the children of Israel wish they had died? _____

6. Who besides Joshua wanted the people to trust God? _____

7. What did the people want to use to kill the two God-fearing explorers?

   _____

8. For how many years would Israel have to wander in the desert?

   _____

9. What did the Lord send among the people to punish them?

   _____

10. Who prayed for the people?

   _____

Draw a line under the word or phrase that answers the question.

1. After how many days did the explorers return from Canaan?

   (20—30—40—50)

2. Which words show that the land was a good land?

   (grasshoppers—milk and honey—fruit trees—grapes)

3. How did the people want to kill Joshua and Caleb?

   (stone them—burn them—hang them—drown them)

4. Who of the older Israelites would get into Canaan?

   (Moses—Miriam—Joshua—Aaron)

5. How long were the Israelites to wander in the desert?

   (10 years—20 years—30 years—40 years)

6. Who sent venomous snakes among the people?

   (God—Moses—Joshua—Caleb)

7. Of what was the serpent made that Moses set upon a pole?

   (iron—tin—clay—bronze)

8. What saved the people from dying of snake bites?

   (bronze snake—Moses—the cross—medicine)

Israel Enters Canaan

(Deuteronomy 34; Joshua 1–5)

Thinking about God's Word

1. Just as Israel was about to enter Canaan, what did the Lord show Moses from Mount Nebo? What happened to Moses then? Why does no one know where the grave of Moses is?

2. Why did the Lord not permit His servant Moses to go into the Promised Land? See Numbers 20:7–12.

3. Whom had the Lord chosen to lead Israel now?

4. List the directions God gave the new leader. How would he be successful?

5. When the people were ready to enter the land, who went first? Why was this proper?

6. How was it possible for the Israelites to pass over the Jordan on dry ground?

7. When did the waters of the Jordan flow as before?

8. Why did the manna now stop falling from heaven?

9. What are some promises God has made to you? How can you be sure that God will keep them?

Working with God's Word

Fill in the blanks.

1. Moses climbed up Mount

   _____.

2. No one knows where Moses'

   _____ is.

3. The Israelites grieved for Moses

   _____ days.

4. God told Joshua, "Do not let this Book of the _____ depart from your mouth."

5. Joshua told the officers, " _____ days from now you will cross the Jordan."

6. The Israelites crossed over the _____ River.

7. The priests carried the

   _____.

8. The water flowing down to the _____ Sea was cut off.

Draw a line under the word or phrase that makes each sentence true.

1. Moses died on Mount (Nebo—Sinai—Carmel—Hermon).

2. (Joshua—The children of Israel—The Lord—Aaron) buried Moses.

3. The children of Israel grieved the death of Moses (30—40—50—60) days.

4. (Caleb—Aaron—Joshua—Moses) was chosen by God to lead the children of Israel into Canaan.

5. Joshua said, "(Three-Four-Five-Six) days from now you will cross the Jordan."

6. The Israelites had to cross the (Salt Sea—Jordan—Red Sea—Nile) to get into the Promised Land.

30

The Conquest of Canaan

(Joshua 6–10)

Thinking about God's Word

1. How did the children of Israel show their faith in God's plan to take Jericho?
2. What happened to Jericho?
3. By what miracle did the Lord make a complete victory possible?
4. How can you tell that the Lord provided Israel with everything they needed in the Promised Land? Which promise of God to Abraham was now completely fulfilled? Which greater promise was not yet fulfilled?

Working with God's Word

Answer the questions.

1. Which city did the Lord tell Joshua to take? _____

2. How many days were the armed men to go around the city one time?

   _____

3. When were the armed men of war to circle the city seven times?

   _____

4. What noise did the people make on the seventh day? _____

   _____

5. Why was it easy for the Israelites to go into the city?_____

   _____

6. Why did Joshua not have to fear the five kings of the Amorites?

   _____

7. How did the Lord kill many of Israel's enemies? _____

8. With which words did Joshua make the day longer? _____

Answer each question with Yes or No.

1. Did the armed men march around the city seven times each day?
   Yes   No

2. Did the Israelites walk around Jericho 13 times?
   Yes   No

3. Did the armed men blow their trumpets?
   Yes   No

4. Did it take two weeks to capture Jericho?
   Yes   No

5. Did five kings of the Amorites join forces against Israel?
   Yes   No

6. Did Joshua say, "O sun, stand still"?
   Yes   No

7. Did the Lord give Israel the land of their forefathers?
   Yes   No

8. Was Joshua the leader of Israel?
   Yes   No

Gideon

(Judges 6)

Thinking about God's Word

1. After the Lord had mercifully brought the children of Israel back to Canaan, what did they do?
2. How did the Lord punish them?
3. How did the Midianites hurt Israel?
4. How did Israel show that they were sorry for what they had done?
5. What did the Lord want Gideon to do?
6. Why did the Lord want the army of Israel reduced to 300?
7. In the words of their battlecry, how did Gideon's men show that they believed God would help them? How did God show them that their faith was not in vain?
8. How did Israel call upon the Lord's name when in trouble?

Working with God's Word

Answer each question with one word.

1. What did the children of Israel do in the eyes of the Lord? _____

2. Into whose hands did the Lord deliver Israel? _____

3. Where was Gideon threshing wheat? _____

4. Who appeared to Gideon? _____

5. Whom did Gideon send to gather the people? _____

6. How many were afraid to fight? _____

7. How many men did the Lord use to save Israel? _____

8. How many men were in each company? _____

9. Who won the battle? _____

Draw a line under the word or phrase that answers each question.

1. Into whose hands did the Lord give Israel? (Philistines—Amorites—Ammonites—Midianites)

2. What was Gideon doing at the winepress? (making wine—pressing grapes—herding sheep—threshing wheat)

3. How many Israelites were afraid to fight? (22,000—300—32,000—10,000)

4. How many were used by God to defeat the Midianites? (22,000—300—32,000—10,000)

5. Into how many companies did Gideon divide his army? (1—2—3—300—4)

6. How did the Midianites lay along in the valley? (like dogs—like locusts—like flies—like giants)

7. In which hand did the Israelites hold their torches? (left—right—both)

8. Who caused the men to turn their swords on each other? (Gideon—Midianites—Israel—God)

32

Samson (Part 1)
(Judges 13–14)

Thinking about God's Word

1. Why did the Lord give Israel to the Philistines? Read the answer in Judges 13:1.
2. What message did the Angel of the Lord bring to Manoah's wife? What was Manoah's son to do?
3. Whom did Samson want permission to marry? Why didn't Samson's father and mother like his marriage to a Philistine girl? Why did the Lord permit the marriage?
4. How did Samson show his strength when a young lion came toward him? How can you tell that it really was not Samson who killed the lion?
5. What riddle did Samson give his companions? What should Samson's wife have done when the 30 men threatened to burn her and her father's household? What would you have done?
6. How did Samson's wife break the Sixth Commandment?

Working with God's Word

Answer each question on the blank lines.

1. Into whose hands did the Lord deliver the Israelites for 40 years? _____

2. To whom did the Angel of the Lord appear? _____

3. What was the child named? _____

4. Where did Samson find a wife?

    _____

5. What did Samson kill near Timnah?

    _____

6. To how many companions did Samson tell a riddle? _____

7. How did Samson's wife get the answer to the riddle? _____

8. Where did Samson get the clothes to give to the men? _____

Fill in the blanks with words from below.

1. Samson's father's name was

    _____.

2. Samson was a _____ unto the Lord.

3. The _____ of the Lord moved in Samson.

4. Samson went down to _____.

5. Samson tore apart the lion as he might have torn apart a _____.

6. Thirty _____ came to Samson's feast.

7. Samson's riddle was answered in _____ days.

8. Samson struck down _____ men and took their clothes.

companions	thirty	seven
goat	Nazirite	Manoah
Timnah	Spirit	

33

Samson (Part 2)

(Judges 15–16)

Thinking about God's Word

1. What did the Philistines do to take Samson captive?
2. When the Philistines shouted against Samson, what do you suppose they said?
3. What did the Philistines want Samson's wife to find out for them? How did they get her to find out?
4. What did the Philistines do to Samson?
5. Why was it easy for the Philistines to bind Samson now?
6. Read the words that show that the Philistines worshiped an idol?
7. Who gave Samson the strength to destroy the building? How many people in the building were killed? Which words show that Samson was killed, too?

Working with God's Word

Fill in the blanks.

1. The Philistines went up and _____ in Judah.
2. The people of Judah bound Samson with two new _____.
3. Samson struck down a _____ men with the jaw-bone of a donkey.
4. Samson loved _____, a Philistine woman.
5. Samson said, "No _____ has ever been used on my head."
6. Delilah called a man to shave off the _____ braids of his hair.
7. The Philistines gouged out Samson's _____ and took him to Gaza.
8. The Philistines offered a great sacrifice unto _____.
9. Upon the roof of the temple there were about _____ men and women.
10. Samson took hold of the two central _____.

Draw a line under the correct answer to each question.

1. Where did the Philistines camp? (Gaza—Judah—Reuben—Benjamin)
2. Why had the Philistines come to the Israelites? (to fight—to steal—to find Samson—to inspect)
3. How many men did Samson slay with the jawbone? (300—1,000—2,000—4,000)
4. How many shekels of silver did each of the Philistine rulers promise Delilah? (1,100—1,200—1,300—1,400)
5. How many braids of hair did the man shave off Samson's head? (2—5—17—7)
6. Where did the Philistines put Samson when they got to Gaza? (dungeon—grave—prison—house—ward)
7. Who was the god of the Philistines? (the Lord—Baal—Dagon—Ashoreth)
8. How many people were on the roof of the house? (30,000—3,000—300—400)

34

Ruth

(The Book of Ruth)

Thinking about God's Word

1. When did the famine mentioned in our lesson come over Canaan? See Ruth 1:1.
2. How many persons belonged to the family of Elimelech?
3. Whom did Elimelech's sons marry?
4. After 10 years in the land of Moab, who of Elimelech's family were still living?
5. To which land did Naomi now want to return? What did Ruth answer when Naomi told her daughters-in-law to return to their own homes? Which of these words were a beautiful confession of faith?
6. After the two women settled in Bethlehem, where did Ruth work to provide food for Naomi and herself?
7. Who was Boaz? How did he show favor to Ruth? Why did he favor her? Whose property did Boaz buy?
8. Who was Ruth's grandson? Who was her great-grandson?

Working with God's Word

Answer each question with one word.

1. What came over the land of Israel? _____

2. Who took his wife and two sons to Moab? _____

3. Where did the wives of Mahlon and Chilion come from? _____

4. Who did not go with Naomi to the land of Judah? _____

5. To which town did Ruth and Naomi go? _____

6. Who owned fields in Bethlehem? _____

7. Who became the wife of Boaz? _____

8. Who was Jesse's son? _____

9. What was the relationship of Ruth to David? _____

Draw a line under the word that makes each sentence true.

1. Naomi was the wife of (Elimelech—Mahlon—Chilion—Boaz).

2. Elimelech had (2—3—4—5) sons.

3. Naomi was Ruth's (sister-in-law—daughter-in-law—mother-in-law).

4. Naomi lived in Moab about (5—10—15—20) years.

5. (Ruth—Orpah—Delilah—Miriam) left Naomi to return to her mother's house.

6. Boaz lived in (Bethlehem—Moab—Jerusalem—Jericho).

7. (Ruth—Orpah—Naomi—Boaz) was Ruth's second husband.

8. (Obed—Boaz—Jesse—Elimelech) was the father of David.

35

The Boy Samuel
(1 Samuel 1–4)

Thinking about God's Word

1. Read 1 Samuel 1:10–11. Why was Hannah, the wife of Elkanah, "in bitterness of soul"?
2. To whom did she pray?
3. What did Hannah mean when she said, "If You will"?
   What promise did she make to the Lord?
4. How did the Lord remember Hannah? How does this show that children are a gift of God?
5. What did Hannah name her child? How did she keep her promise?

Working with God's Word

Answer each question.

1. Who were Elkanah's two wives?

   _____

2. Why did Hannah pray to the Lord?

   _____

3. What did Hannah name her son?

   _____

4. Why did Hannah bring Samuel to the house of the Lord?

   _____

5. How was the Lord going to punish Eli and his sons?

   _____

6. What did the Lord tell Samuel while he slept?

   _____

7. Against whom did Israel go to battle?

   _____

8. What happened to the ark of God?

   _____

9. What happened to the Israelites?

   _____

10. What happened to Eli and his two sons? _____

Draw a line through the sentences that are not true.

1. Elkanah had a wife by the name of Hannah.
2. Peninnah was the wife of Elkanah.
3. Hannah called her son Eli.
4. Hannah kept the promise she had made to the Lord.
5. Eli was a good father.
6. Eli was Samuel's teacher.
7. God said to Eli, "Your two sons will both die on the same day."
8. The Philistines took the ark of God.

36

King Saul

(1 Samuel 8–15)

Thinking about God's Word

1. Who was judge of Israel all his life? See 1 Samuel 7:15.
2. Why did the elders tell Samuel they wanted a king? Why was that a sin?
3. Why did Samuel call the tribes of Israel together? *Note:* There were 13 tribes in Israel, one for each son of Jacob except Joseph. He was honored with two tribes named after his two sons, Ephraim and Manasseh. We usually speak of 12 tribes because the sons of Levi did not inherit a province of their own. They were the priests and as such received gifts from the other tribes.
4. How did Saul, the new king, show his humility?
5. Why did Saul immediately have to go to war? What two things made it possible for him to win? Why?
6. What did Samuel tell Saul about sacrifice?

Working with God's Word

Answer each question with one word.

1. Who came to Samuel and asked for a king? _____
2. Whom had Israel rejected? _____
3. Who was chosen as Israel's first king? _____
4. Who came upon Saul? _____
5. Who won the battle against Ammon? _____

6. How much of the Amalekites should Saul destroy? _____
7. Whose instructions did Saul say he performed? _____
8. What had Saul spared besides the sheep? _____
9. What is not so important as obedience? _____

Of whom do you think when you read each of the following sentences?

1. All the elders of Israel came to him. _____
2. He was displeased that Israel wanted a king. _____
3. The first king was the son of Kish. _____
4. They shouted, "Long live the king." _____
5. He said, "I did what the Lord wanted." _____
6. He said, "To obey is better than sacrifice." _____
7. He rejected Saul from being king. _____

49

37

David Is Chosen
(1 Samuel 16–17)

Thinking about God's Word

1. Why did the Lord send Samuel to Jesse?
2. Read the words that tell that David was blessed and Saul was plagued.
3. How did God give David a chance to learn the work of a king?
4. Against whom did Saul and his army have to go to battle again?
5. Why, do you suppose, was Goliath so eager to fight this battle alone with an Israelite? In whom did the giant put his trust? In whom should Israel have trusted?
6. How did David show that he was not frightened by the giant?

Working with God's Word

Write the answers to the following questions.

1. Who was chosen to be the next king? _____

2. How can you tell that God was with David? _____

3. For whom did David play the harp? _____

4. Who gathered their armies against Israel? _____

5. Who was the champion of the Philistines? _____

6. Who was afraid of him? _____

7. How did David help his father? _____

8. What did David call the Philistine giant? _____

9. To whom were the words of David reported? _____

Answer Yes or No.

1. Did David play a violin for Saul?
   Yes   No

2. Did David serve the king?
   Yes   No

3. Was Goliath more than 10 feet tall?
   Yes   No

4. Were Saul and his army afraid of Goliath?
   Yes   No

5. Did Goliath present himself 40 days?
   Yes   No

6. Was David afraid of Goliath?
   Yes   No

7. Did David trust in himself?
   Yes   No

38

David and Goliath

(1 Samuel 17)

Thinking about God's Word

1. How did David prove to Saul that he was not afraid of the giant?
2. What was David's answer to Saul's words? How did David know that the Lord would deliver him? (Think of what he had received from Samuel.)
3. Why didn't David take the armor of Saul? Describe the weapons he did take.
4. Which words of Goliath show that he despised David?
5. With what did Goliath come to David? In whose name did David come to Goliath? Who was better prepared? Why?
6. How did David boldly foretell who would win? Why would God hand Goliath over to David?
7. How did David drop the giant to the ground? How did David kill him?
8. Why did the Philistines flee? Why was it easy for Israel to win now?
9. What important lesson did David teach the army of Israel?

Working with God's Word

Answer each question.

1. What did David say to Saul?

   _____

2. Why didn't Saul think David could win?

   _____

3. Why did David know he could win?

   _____

4. How did Saul wish to protect David?

   _____

5. What things did David use for weapons?

   _____

6. Which words of Goliath show that he thought little of David? _____

   _____

7. What did David show in his words to Goliath?_____

8. Where did the stone strike the giant?

   _____

9. How did David make sure that Goliath would die? _____

10. Who won the battle?

    _____

Are the following sentences true or false?

1. Saul commanded David to fight Goliath.   T   F
2. David belonged to the army of Israel   T   F
3. With the Lord, David could not be beaten.   T   F
4. David was a soldier of the Lord.   T   F
5. David chose five smooth stones.   T   F
6. David carried no real weapon of war.   T   F
7. Goliath trusted in himself.   T   F
8. Goliath trusted in his sword, shield, and spear.   T   F
9. The Lord won the war for Israel.   T   F
10. The First Commandment tells us to trust in God above all things.   T   F

David's Fall and Repentance

(2 Samuel 11–12)

Thinking about God's Word

1. Upon whom did David's army make war?
2. Where should David have been instead of at home in Jerusalem? How did Satan use David's idleness to lead him into sin?
3. Who really killed Uriah? Why?
4. Why did the Lord send Nathan to David? Read what Nathan said to him.
5. If David meant what he said about punishing the rich man, whom would he have had to punish? How was David punished?
6. Which were David's words of repentance?
7. In which words did Nathan announce God's forgiveness to David?

Working with God's Word

Answer each question with one word.

1. Whom did Joab and his servants destroy? _____

2. Who stayed behind in Jerusalem? _____

3. When did David walk upon the roof of his palace? _____

4. Whose wife was Bathsheba? _____

5. Whom did David have killed? _____

6. Whom did David take to be his wife? _____

7. Which man did the Lord send to David? _____

8. Who was the man who took the poor man's lamb? _____

9. What had David done against God? _____

10. Was David's sin forgiven? _____

Fill in the blanks with words from below.

David sent _____ to fight against Ammon and Rabbah, while he stayed in _____. David fell into sin with Bathsheba, the wife of _____. David wanted Bathsheba's husband to _____. After Uriah was dead, David took Bathsheba to be his _____. David said, "I have _____ against the Lord." David's sin was _____ but his child _____.

Nathan	sinned	died
wife	sin	Uriah
Joab	Jerusalem	die
forgiven		

Absalom's Rebellion

(2 Samuel 14–18)

Thinking about God's Word

1. Who was Absalom? For what was he praised?
2. What did Absalom want? Why was this a sin? See Romans 13:9.
3. How did Absalom steal the hearts of the Israelites?
4. What did Absalom tell his father he wanted in Hebron? Which words showed that he wanted to start a rebellion? Find the meaning of the word *rebellion* in your dictionary.
5. Who fled from his son? Who chased after his father?
6. How did the father show his love for his son in spite of his son's unfaithfulness?

Working with God's Word

Fill the blanks with the correct word.

1. Absalom was praised for his

   _____ appearance.

2. Absalom said, "If only I were appointed

   _____ in the land."

3. Absalom said that he wanted to go to

   Hebron to fulfill a _____.

4. David had to _____ from

   Absalom, his son.

5. Absalom came to the city of

   _____.

6. David crossed over the river

   _____.

7. Joab killed Absalom with three

   _____.

8. Absalom was buried in a

   _____.

9. Absalom's body was covered with

   _____.

Draw a line under the word or phrase that makes each sentence true.

1. David was Absalom's (brother— father—servant—general).
2. Absalom said he wanted to go to (Jerusalem—Jordan—Bethlehem— Hebron) to fulfill a vow.
3. Despising the government is sinning against the (Third—Fourth—Ninth— Tenth) Commandment.
4. David and his people fled across the (Nile—Kishon—Jordan—Tigris).
5. Absalom fled (on a mule—on a horse—in a chariot—in a wagon).
6. Absalom's head caught in the boughs of (a maple—a pine—an oak—a sycamore).
7. Joab killed Absalom with (2—3—4—5) javelins.
8. Absalom's body was covered with (earth—stones—water—grass).

41

Solomon and the Temple
(1 Kings 3–8)

Thinking about God's Word

1. Who was Solomon's father?
2. What special favor did Solomon ask for?
3. What did the Lord give Solomon that was more than he asked for?
4. What should Solomon do to have a long life?
5. What did Solomon build?
6. How long did it take to build?
7. What did Solomon ask the Lord to do for the people of Israel?

Working with God's Word

Answer each question correctly.

1. Who sat upon the throne of David, his father? _____

2. How did the Lord appear to Solomon?
   _____

3. For what did Solomon ask the Lord?
   _____

4. What did the Lord give Solomon?
   _____

5. How long did it take to build the house of the Lord? _____

6. Where did the priests put the ark of the covenant? _____

7. Who said the prayer before the altar of the Lord? _____

8. What should the Lord do for those who sinned against Him?

   _____

Draw a line under the word or phrase that answers the question correctly.

1. How was Solomon related to David? (father—son—brother—uncle)

2. How did the Lord appear to Solomon? (in person—through angels—in a dream—through the Bible)

3. What did Solomon call himself before the Lord? (king—priest—servant—man)

4. What did Solomon pray for? (honor—riches—wisdom—a great kingdom)

5. Where was the ark of the covenant placed? (in the palace—in the Most Holy Place—in the court)

6. What name did Solomon call God in his prayer? (Jehovah—God—Almighty—Lord God of Israel)

The Prophet Elijah

(1 Kings 16–17)

Thinking about God's Word

1. Ahab was the seventh king of Israel. Which words tell that he was one of the most wicked kings?

2. How did the Lord try to bring Ahab to repentance?

3. Why was "neither dew nor rain" a terrible punishment? How long would the curse last? Which words tell that rain would fall again only at God's command?

4. How did the Lord take care of His servant Elijah? Why?

5. Why was it not only a miracle that food was brought to Elijah, but also that *ravens* brought the food?

6. Why did Elijah leave the brook in the Kerith Ravine?

7. Why was it strange that the Lord should command a widow to feed His prophet?

8. Why was Elijah's request for water hard to grant?

9. Why would this widow not have to fear? How can you tell that she believed?

10. How was Elijah able to bring the widow's son back from death?

Working with God's Word

Fill in the blanks.

1. Ahab was the king of _____.

2. Ahab sinned against God by worshiping _____.

3. _____, the prophet, talked to Ahab.

4. God held back _____ from Ahab's land.

5. Elijah hid near the Ravine _____.

6. Ravens brought Elijah _____ and meat.

7. The Lord told Elijah to go to the city of _____.

8. A _____ took care of Elijah in this city.

9. God fed the whole family with _____ and oil.

10. _____ gives us all our food.

Draw a line through the sentences that are not true.

1. Ahab was king of Israel.

2. Ahab sinned against God by worshiping the god Dagon.

3. God sent rain to the earth.

4. The Lord commanded Elijah to hide at the Kerith Ravine.

5. Ravens brought food in the morning and evening to Elijah.

6. Elijah went to the home of a widow in Zebulon.

7. Elijah gathered sticks near the village of Zarephath.

8. Elijah asked the widow for a drink of water.

9. The Lord gave the widow money to buy food.

10. Elijah brought the widow's husband back from the dead.

43

Elijah and the Prophets of Baal
(1 Kings 18)

Thinking about God's Word

1. Whom were the people worshiping besides God?
2. How did Elijah put the idol Baal to a test?
3. What showed that the idol Baal had no power?
4. How did Elijah make it harder for fire to burn his altar? On whom did he call?
5. How can you tell that the fire that fell from heaven was truly a fire sent by God?
6. How did the people confess that Elijah had won the test?
7. Why did the people now do as Elijah commanded?
8. How did Elijah get rid of the heathen prophets?

Working with God's Word

Which of the following sentences are not taken from the story?

1. Elijah said, "If the Lord is God, follow Him."
2. Elijah said, "Get two bulls for us."
3. They called on Dagon all day long.
4. He repaired the altar of the Lord that was broken down.
5. Elijah took 12 stones and built an altar.
6. He dug a trench around the altar.
7. The water ran down around the altar and even filled the trench.
8. Let it be known that I have done all these things at Your Word.

9. Answer me, O Lord; answer me!
10. Then the fire of the Lord fell and burned up the sacrifice.

Fill in the blanks with words from below.

_____ preached to the people. He said, "If the _____ is God, follow Him; but if _____ is God, follow him." The prophets of Baal prepared a _____. Elijah did likewise. Then the prophets of Baal called to Baal from _____ till noon. But Baal did not answer. When Elijah prayed to the Lord, fire fell from _____. It burned the bull, the wood, the stones, and the soil and licked up the _____. The people then fell down and _____ God. But Elijah took the prophets of Baal to the _____ Valley and slaughtered them.

heaven	Baal	Lord
morning	water	bull
praised	Kishon	fire
Elijah		

44

Naboth's Vineyard

(1 Kings 21)

Thinking about God's Word

1. For what purpose did Ahab say he wanted Naboth's vineyard? How did he intend to get it?
2. Why would it have been a sin for Naboth to trade or sell his land? See Numbers 36:7.
3. How did the king act like a small child?
4. Who was Jezebel? What promise did she make the king?
5. What was her scheme for getting the vineyard?
6. Why could Ahab now take possession of the vineyard?
7. Where did the Lord tell Elijah to go?
8. What was Elijah to say to Ahab?

Working with God's Word

Answer each question.

1. Where was Naboth's vineyard?

   _____

2. What did King Ahab want?

   _____

3. Why couldn't Naboth sell his vineyard?

   _____

4. Who said she would get the vineyard?

   _____

5. What were the false witnesses to say against Naboth? _____

6. How was Naboth put to death?

   _____

7. Whom did the Lord send to Ahab?

   _____

8. Where would Ahab die? _____

9. Where and how would Jezebel die?

   _____

10. Which words say that Elijah's words came true? _____

Draw a line under the correct answer to each question.

1. What did Ahab want from Naboth? (house—vineyard—garden—grapes)
2. Against which commandment is coveting a sin? (Seventh—Fifth—Ninth—Eighth)
3. How had Naboth gotten his property? (bought it—earned it—inheritance—stole it)
4. Who was a wicked woman? (Jezebel—Bathsheba—Sarah—Ruth)
5. To whom were the letters sent? (priests—elders—princes—soldiers)
6. Against which commandment do false witnesses sin? (Seventh—Fifth—Ninth—Eighth)
7. Who took Naboth's property after he died? (Ahab—Jezebel—Elijah—Solomon)
8. Whom did the dogs eat? (Jezebel—Naboth—Elijah—Ahab)

45

Elisha Sees Elijah Ascend

(2 Kings 2)

Thinking about God's Word

1. How was the Lord going to take Elijah into heaven?
2. Who went with Elijah to cross the River Jordan? How did they get across?
3. Elijah was Elisha's teacher. After Elijah ascended into heaven, Elisha was to be prophet in his place. How did Elisha's answer to his teacher show that he knew what he needed to take Elijah's place?
4. In what form did the angels of heaven come to get Elijah? Where did the chariot and horses of fire come from?
5. Who saw this miracle? What did he call after Elijah?
6. By what miracle did the Lord show Elisha that He was with him?
7. What did the prophets of Jericho now say of Elisha? What did they mean? How did they know? See 2 Kings 2:14–15.

Working with God's Word

Answer each question with one word.

1. Where did the Lord want to take Elijah? _____

2. Who walked with Elijah? _____

   _____

3. With what did Elijah hit the water?

   _____

4. For how big a portion of Elijah's spirit did Elisha ask? _____

5. In what did Elijah ride to heaven?

   _____

6. Over which river did Elisha cross?

   _____

Answer each question with Yes or No.

1. Was Elijah a true servant of God?
   Yes   No

2. Did the waters part for Elijah?
   Yes   No

3. Did Elijah ask for a double portion of Elisha's spirit?
   Yes   No

4. Did Elijah go up by a whirlwind to heaven?
   Yes   No

5. Did Elisha cry, "My father, my father, the chariot and horsemen of Israel!"
   Yes   No

6. Did Elisha strike the waters with his cloak?
   Yes   No

7. Did the prophets live in Bethel?
   Yes   No

46

Naaman and Elisha
(2 Kings 5)

Thinking about God's Word

1. Who was Naaman?
2. What was wrong with him?
3. What did the servant girl say?
4. Why did Naaman take money and clothing to Samaria? How did he travel?
5. How did Elisha humble Naaman?
6. How did the servants persuade their master to try Elisha's cure? What happened?
7. In which words did Naaman admit that God of Israel had cured him? How did he want to reward Elisha? Why do you suppose Elisha refused the reward?

Working with God's Word

Fill in the blanks.

1. _____ was commander of the army of the king of Aram.

2. _____ had leprosy.

3. A _____ served Naaman's wife.

4. Naaman was told to wash in the _____ river seven times.

5. Naaman thought the rivers of _____ were better than the rivers of Israel.

6. _____ was a servant of Elisha.

7. Naaman gave Gehazi _____ talents of silver.

8. Gehazi said to Elisha, "Your servant _____ go anywhere."

9. Gehazi became a _____.

Draw a line through the sentences that are not true.

1. Naaman was king of Syria.

2. A servant girl told Naaman to go to Samaria.

3. Naaman took much gold, silver, and clothing on his trip to Samaria.

4. Elisha did not go out to see Naaman when he came to Samaria to be healed.

5. Naaman dipped himself into the Jordan River six times.

6. Naaman became a believer in the true God.

7. Gehazi was Naaman's servant.

8. Gehazi was punished for coveting, lying, and deceiving.

59

47

God Sends Jonah
(Jonah 1–3)

Thinking about God's Word

1. Who was Jonah?
2. Where did the Lord tell Jonah to go? Why?
3. Why did Jonah get on a ship?
4. Whom was Jonah trying to get away from?
5. What did Jonah tell the sailors to do?
6. Where was Jonah for three days and three nights?
7. How did Jonah survive?
8. In what way is the story of Jonah and the story of Jesus the same?

Working with God's Word

Fill in the blanks with words from below.

1. Jonah said, "Pick me up and throw me into the _____."

2. A great _____ swallowed Jonah.

3. Jonah prayed, "In my distress I called to the _____."

4. The Lord told Jonah to go to the city of _____.

5. The people of Nineveh were _____.

6. The people of Nineveh would be overturned in _____ days.

7. The Ninevites declared a _____.

8. The Ninevites put on _____.

fast	sackcloth	wicked
fish	sea	40
30	Lord	Nineveh

Draw a line under the word that makes each sentence true.

1. Jonah was the son of (David—Micah—Amittai—Joshua).

2. The great city of Ninevah was (good—wicked—new—poor).

3. The Lord sent a (wind—rainbow—boat—sailor) on the sea.

4. When Jonah was thrown overboard, the sea grew (choppy—calm—rough—deep).

5. Twice the Lord told Jonah to go to (Jerusalem—Syria—Samaria—Ninevah).

6. It took (1—2—3—4) days to get there.

7. God had (vengeance—pity—compassion—mercy) on the people in the city.

48

Jeremiah
(Jeremiah 37–38)

Thinking about God's Word

1. What did Jeremiah tell the king of Judah?
2. What did the officials say to the king?
3. Where did the officials put Jeremiah?
4. What did they hope would happen to him?
5. What did Ebed-Melech say to the king?
6. How many men helped Jeremiah?
7. How did they save him?

Working with God's Word

Put a line through the sentences that are not true.

1. Jeremiah was a prophet.

2. The word of the Lord came to Jeremiah.

3. Jeremiah was to tell the king, "Pharaoh's army … will go back to its own land, to Egypt."

4. The Amorites were going to return to attack the city.

5. Jeremiah spoke to King Hezekiah.

6. They put Jeremiah into a stream.

7. They wanted Jeremiah to starve.

8. Twenty men rescued Jeremiah.

49

The Three Men in the Fiery Furnace
(Daniel 3)

Thinking about God's Word

1. How did Nebuchadnezzar sin against the First Commandment? Whom did he gather to come to the dedication?
2. How did the king force the people to commit idolatry? How did he threaten to punish them if they disobeyed?
3. Who did not obey the command of the king?
4. What did the king say to the three men? What did they answer?
5. Were the three men sure that God *could* save them? Give a reason. Did the three men know whether God *wanted* to save them? Give a reason.
6. Why was Nebuchadnezzar astonished when he looked into the furnace? What did he say?
7. Who was the fourth man in the furnace?
8. What words show that the men were not hurt?
9. How did the king now confess that the Lord was stronger than he?

Working with God's Word

Answer each question on the blank lines.

1. What did King Nebuchadnezzar have made of gold? _____

2. Why did he have the image made? _____

3. How were those who did not worship the image to be punished? _____

4. Which three men did not pray to the image? _____

5. In whom did they have faith to deliver them? _____

6. Why did the king have the furnace made seven times hotter? _____

7. What was done with the three men before they were thrown into the furnace? _____

8. Who was the fourth man in the furnace? _____

9. Why do you think he had gone into the flames? _____

Draw a line under the correct answer to each question.

1. Who was king?
   (Naaman—Ahab—Nebuchadnezzar—Saul)

2. What did the king have made? (palace—temple—image—cornet)

3. Of what was the idol made?
   (silver—gold—brass—iron)

4. What gave the signal for worshiping the idol?
   (whistle—music—cornet—light)

5. To which people did the three men belong?
   (Chaldeans—Syrians—Jews—Babylonians)

6. How many were thrown into the furnace?
   (1—2—3—4)

7. How many times hotter did the king order the furnace made?
   (7—6—2—9)

8. How many people did the king see in the furnace?
   (1—2—3—4)

9. In which book of the Bible is this lesson written?
   (1 Kings—2 Kings—2 Samuel—Daniel)

50

Daniel in the Lions' Den
(Daniel 6)

Thinking about God's Word

1. Who was jealous of Daniel? Why did they want him out of the way?
2. Why could the princes find no grounds for charges against Daniel? How did they believe they could trap him?
3. What edict did they persuade the king to sign?
4. To whom did Daniel always pray? How was that against the king's decree?
5. Who reported Daniel's worship to the king?
6. How can you tell that the king thought highly of Daniel? Which words of the king show that Daniel must have told Darius about the God of Israel?
7. How did Daniel say that God had protected him?
8. How did the desire to kill Daniel bring death upon the administrators? How did Darius now honor the God of Daniel? Was Darius' new law a good one?

Working with God's Word

Answer each question with one word.

1. Which king set three administrators over his kingdom? _____
2. Why could the administrators find no fault in Daniel? _____
3. For how many days was the edict to hold? _____
4. How many times a day did Daniel pray? _____
5. Where were the lions to which Daniel was thrown? _____

6. Who saved Daniel from the mouths of the lions? _____
7. Who was glad when he saw that Daniel was safe? _____
8. To whom did Darius want the people to pray now? _____

Draw a line under the answer that makes each sentence true.

1. (Nebuchadnezzar—David—Darius—Daniel) was the king of the land.
2. The king made Daniel (a ruler—a king—a prince—an administrator) in the land.
3. The administrators were (faithful to—jealous of—kind to—loving to) Daniel.
4. No man was to pray to anyone except (God—the king—Daniel—the princes).
5. This law was to last for (10—3—20—30) days.
6. The king signed (an edict—a book—a petition—a dominion).
7. Daniel prayed (10—3—20—30) times a day.
8. Daniel was thrown into a (den—fiery furnace—prison—pit).
9. The king let Daniel be thrown to the lions because he (hated Daniel—could not change the law—wished to please the princes—wanted Daniel killed).
10. (Daniel—Darius—God's angel—The king) saved Daniel from the lions.

A Message for Zechariah

(Luke 1)

Thinking About God's Word

1. What is a messenger? Why is John a messenger for Jesus?
2. Why was Gabriel sent to tell Zechariah about a son?
3. Which words show that Gabriel came from God in answer to Zechariah's prayer?
4. Why did Zechariah ask, "How can I be sure of this?"
5. Why is it sometimes hard for us to believe what God says?
6. Who is "the Lord" whom John went before?
7. Name two other Bible women who were blessed with children only after they had become very old.

Working with God's Word

Answer each question.

1. What great event was drawing near at the time of this lesson?

   _____

2. Which words tell that Zechariah and Elizabeth were God-fearing?

   _____

3. Which Bible words tell that the couple was very old?_____

4. Why was this old couple not completely happy? _____

5. Where did Zechariah burn incense to the Lord? _____

6. Who appeared to Zechariah as he was burning incense? _____

7. What good news did an angel bring from God to Zechariah? _____

8. Which words tell what great work John was to perform? _____

9. In which words did Zechariah show his doubt of God's promise?

   _____

10. What happened to Zechariah because he doubted the promise?

    _____

Answer each question correctly with one word from below.

1. Who was Zechariah's wife?

   _____

2. In which building was Zechariah burning incense? _____

3. On which side of the altar did the angel stand? _____

4. What was Zechariah's child to be named? _____

5. Like which great prophet was the child to be? _____

6. What was the name of the angel?

   _____

7. For whom was the child to be a messenger? _____

Gabriel	Temple	Elizabeth
Jesus	Elijah	John
left	Mary	Michael
right	Moses	

The Announcement to Mary

(Luke 1; Matthew 1)

Thinking about God's Word

1. Which words of the lesson show that the Savior was to be true man, born of a woman? What was to be His work?

2. Why was Mary afraid of the angel at first?

3. With which words did Mary say that she was a servant of God?

4. Which words show that God, not Joseph, was to be the true Father of Jesus?

5. Why was it necessary for the world's Savior to be a human?

6. What was the Savior to be named, according to the angel's words? Find three other names for Jesus from this lesson.

Working with God's Word

Answer each question.

1. To whom was Gabriel sent?

   _____

2. What words did Gabriel use to greet Mary? _____

3. What was the good news the angel brought to Mary? _____

4. What name was to be given to the Child? _____

5. In which words did Mary say that she could not understand it all?

   _____

6. In which words did the angel say that God can do everything? _____

7. How did Mary show that she believed the angel's words?_____

8. How did Joseph learn of God's wonderful promise?_____

9. How did Joseph show that he believed God's promise? _____

By drawing a line from word to word, match all the words given below with their meanings.

Words	Meanings
pledged	rule
virgin	thought about
favored	greatly honored
wondered	promised
reign	woman who has not had sexual intercourse

The Birth of John the Baptist

(Luke 1)

Thinking about God's Word

1. How did God's promise to Zechariah and Elizabeth come true?
2. Which words show that Elizabeth's neighbors and cousins knew that the child came from God?
3. In the naming of their son, how did the parents show that they had learned to obey and trust God without question?
4. When our wisdom and learning advise us to do the opposite of what God wants, to whom must we listen? Why?
5. How did Zechariah use his loosed tongue, which once had spoken words of doubt at God's promise?
6. How can you show your thankfulness to God for having kept His promises?

Working with God's Word

Answer each question.

1. What promise had the angel Gabriel given Zechariah in the temple?

   _____

2. How were the angel's words fulfilled?

   _____

3. What did the parents do eight days after John was born?

   _____

4. On what day was the child publicly given a name? _____

5. How did Zechariah settle the matter of naming the child?_____

6. For what purpose did Zechariah use his tongue after it was loosed?

   _____

7. What did Zechariah prophesy about his son? _____

8. Where was John until the day he appeared to Israel? _____

Answer each question with one word from below.

1. On which day as the baby circumcised?

   _____

2. What did the neighbors want to name the baby? _____

3. What did the mother name him?

   _____

4. What did the father name him?

   _____

5. Whose command did the parents obey?

   _____

6. For whom was this child to prepare the way? _____

7. Who asked for a writing tablet?

   _____

8. Where did John go before he appeared to Israel? _____

9. What special power did the Holy Spirit give Zechariah?_____

Zechariah	eighth	Paul
baptize	mountain	desert
God's	prophesy	Jesus
John	40th	80th

54

The Birth of Jesus
(Luke 2)

Thinking about God's Word

1. Name three prophecies about the Savior's coming made by Old Testament prophets.
2. Who was Caesar Augustus?
3. How did God use Caesar Augustus to bring Mary and Joseph to the place where Jesus was to be born?
4. Which simple words tell how the Savior of the world was born at Bethlehem?
5. What difference would it make to us if Jesus had not been born?
6. How do you know that Jesus was born?
7. Who gave the Christ Child to us as a gift of love? Find the answer in John 3:16.
8. Of what should the giving of presents at Christmas remind Christians?
9. Why is the birth of Jesus the greatest event that ever happened?

Working with God's Word

Answer each question.

1. What great time in the world's history now had come?

   _____

2. What new law did the Roman emperor make for the Roman world?

   _____

3. Who had chosen this time to fulfill His promises?

   _____

4. Where was each person to go to be taxed?

   _____

5. What was the name of the city to which Joseph and Mary went?

   _____

6. To whose family did Mary and Joseph belong?

   _____

7. What great happiness came to Mary in Bethlehem?

   _____

8. In what did Mary wrap her Child?

   _____

9. Where was the newborn Baby laid?

   _____

10. Who was this Child?

   _____

Draw a line under the word that makes each sentence true.

1. (Augustus—Quirinius—Julius) was the emperor at the time of Jesus' birth.

2. The emperor made a law that all (Romans—Jews—the world) should be taxed.

3. (Caesar Augustus—Quirinius—Julius) was the governor of Syria when Jesus was born.

4. Everyone had to go to (Rome—Bethlehem—his own city) to be taxed.

5. Joseph and Mary were descendants of King (David—Saul—Ahab).

6. (Jerusalem—Nazareth—Bethlehem) was the city of David.

7. Jesus was born in (a palace—an inn—a stable—a barn).

8. Mary laid her Baby (in a cradle—on the ground—in a manger).

9. Mary and Joseph had come from (Syria—Jerusalem—Nazareth) to be taxed.

10. (David—Joseph—God) was the true Father of the Child Jesus.

55

Angels Announce the Savior's Birth
(Luke 2)

Thinking about God's Word

1. What kind of birth announcement did God send when Jesus was born?
2. How did God show that He wanted the good news of His Son's birth to be known by the common, ordinary people?
3. What was good about the news that the angel brought?
4. Which words show that the good news was meant for all the people in the world?
5. What song of praise did the angels sing to God for His goodness?
6. What is the peace that Jesus would bring?
7. What did the shepherds do after they had heard and seen the angels?
8. Which words show that Mary, the mother of Jesus, remembered all these events?
9. Who told you the good news of how Jesus was born for you? How can you show your thankfulness for having been told these wonderful things?

Working with God's Word

On the blank lines write a few words from the Bible story that answer the following questions.

1. Where were the shepherds?

   _____

2. When did the angel appear?

   _____

3. What shone around the shepherd?

   _____

4. Who had been born this day?

   _____

5. Where did the angels come from?

   _____

6. How do you know the shepherds believed the angel?

   _____

7. Where did the shepherds find the Baby lying?

   _____

8. What did the shepherds do after they saw Jesus?

   _____

9. How did Mary remember and think about these things?

   _____

Fill in the blanks with words from below.

1. There were shepherds in the _____ near Bethlehem.

2. They were watching over their _____ during the night.

3. When the angel appeared, the shepherds were _____.

4. But the angel said, "Do not be afraid. I bring you good _____."

5. The angel called the newborn Child a _____.

6. A great company of the heavenly _____ sang a song of praise.

7. The shepherds found the Baby lying in a _____.

8. The shepherds spread the _____ about Jesus.

9. Mary treasured up all these things and _____ them in her heart.

10. The shepherds could be called the first _____.

missionaries	host	flocks
pondered	fields	Joseph
word	Savior	Bethlehem
manger	news	terrified

The Presentation of Jesus

(Luke 2)

Thinking about God's Word

1. How did Jesus' parents keep the law of Moses for Him when He was eight days old? Which law did they obey when He was 40 days old?

2. What name was given to the Savior at the time of His circumcision? What is the meaning of that name?

3. Who is meant by the "salvation" of which Simeon spoke? How is Jesus your salvation?

4. Why was Simeon ready to die after having seen Jesus? Why can you die without fear, just as Simeon was able to do?

Working with God's Word

Answer each question.

1. What law of God was fulfilled in Jesus when He was eight days old?

   _____

2. How long did Mary wait before bringing Jesus to the temple?

   _____

3. Where did Jesus' parents go to present Him to the Lord? _____

4. Who was waiting for the Savior's coming in Jerusalem? _____

5. Which words tell that he was a God-fearing man?

   _____

6. What special promise had been given him by the Holy Spirit?

   _____

7. Why was Simeon in the temple on this day? _____

8. In which words did Simeon say that the Lord had kept His promise?

   _____

9. Which of Simeon's words say that Jesus is the Savior of all people?

   _____

10. Who marveled at the words of Simeon?

    _____

Draw a line under the word or phrase that makes each sentence true.

1. Jesus was (born—circumcised—promised) on the eighth day.

2. Jesus was presented at the temple (in Nazareth—in Jerusalem—in Bethlehem).

3. (Forty—Thirty—Twenty) days after His birth Jesus was presented to the Lord.

4. Joseph and Mary took Jesus to (Bethlehem—Nazareth—Jerusalem) when He was 40 days old.

5. Simeon lived in (Jerusalem—Galilee—Bethlehem—Hebron).

6. The Holy Spirit had told Simeon that before his death he would (become very old—preach in the temple—see the Savior).

7. Simeon was (late and old—righteous and devout—very sad).

8. Simeon said that Jesus was (a great king—not a heathen—salvation).

57

The Magi from the East

(Matthew 2)

Thinking about God's Word

1. Who were the people from the East who came to see Jesus?
2. Why did the Magi come to seek Jesus at this time?
3. What led them from their land to the Holy Land? Why did they need a star to guide them?
4. How did the chief priests and scribes of Jesus' time discover where the Savior was to be born? See Micah 5:2 in your Bible.
5. Who said to the Magi, "Go and make a careful search for the Child"?
6. Why did Herod ask the Magi to let him know where the Child was to be found? Why did God warn the Magi not to tell Herod where Jesus was?

Working with God's Word

Answer each question.

1. Who came from the East to visit Jesus?

   _____

2. What are the Magi also called?

   _____

3. Why did they wish to see Jesus?

   _____

4. Why was Herod disturbed at the words of the Magi? _____

5. From whom did Herod learn where Jesus was to be born? _____

6. What answer was given Herod when he wished to know Jesus' birthplace?

   _____

7. How did the Wise Men find the home where Jesus lived? _____

8. How did the Magi show that they believed Jesus to be God?

   _____

9. With which gifts did they show their love to the Savior? _____

10. How did God keep the Wise Men from returning to Herod?_____

Answer each question with the words from below.

1. From where did the Wise Men come?

   _____

2. At which city did they stop for information? _____

3. What did the Wise Men call Jesus?

   _____

4. Who was troubled about the Wise Men's question? _____

5. What led the Wise Men from the East?

   _____

6. Whom did the Wise Men find with the Child? _____

7. How did God warn the Magi not to see Herod? _____

Mary	aloes	Jerusalem
Nazareth	East	by an angel
King of the Jews		by a dream
Herod	Persia	star

73

The Escape to Egypt
(Matthew 2)

Thinking about God's Word

1. Jeremiah prophesied the "Slaughter of the Innocents" which took place at this time. In what respect were the boys in Bethlehem innocent?

2. How might one of the gifts which the Magi brought to Jesus have been put to good use at this time?

3. Why should God's children be happy to know that the angels are always near them? How did God use angels in this story?

4. What does it mean to you to know that God kept all His promises and prophecies in Jesus?

5. How did God defend Jesus against all danger and guard and protect Him from all evil? How does God do the same for you daily?

6. How many other Bible people can you name who lived in Egypt? By whom were the ancestors of Jesus led out of Egypt?

Working with God's Word

Fill in the blanks.

1. The angel of the Lord appeared to _____ in a dream.

2. God wanted Jesus to escape to _____.

3. Herod was seeking the young Child to _____ Him.

4. Joseph traveled with the young Child and the mother during the _____.

5. Herod killed boys that were _____ years old and under.

6. An angel of the Lord appeared in a dream to Joseph in _____.

7. Joseph was told to take Mary and Jesus back to the land of _____.

8. They returned and lived in a city called _____.

The Boy Jesus at the Temple

(Luke 2)

Thinking about God's Word

1. When Jesus was 12 years old, where did His parents take Him?
2. Which words tell that Jesus' parents were faithful worshipers at the temple?
3. Where did Jesus say He had been while His parents looked for Him?
4. Read Colossians 2:3. How did the teachers in the temple find the words to be true?
5. Why did Jesus study Scripture even though "all the treasures of wisdom and knowledge" are to be found in Him?
6. Which words tell that Mary and Joseph were very worried over the thought of losing Jesus?
7. What reason did Jesus give for staying behind in Jerusalem?
8. What has been offered to you to help you in learning and knowing Scripture? Name people and things that have helped you.
9. Two commandments of God were clearly obeyed by Jesus in this lesson. What are they? How did Jesus obey them? How can you follow His example?

Working with God's Word

Answer each question.

1. What great festival did Jesus' parents attend each year? _____

2. Where was this festival held?

   _____

3. Why did the parents not worry over Jesus' absence on the return trip?

   _____

4. How long did Joseph and Mary look for Jesus before finding Him?

   _____

5. Where was Jesus all this time?

   _____

6. What was it about Jesus that amazed all who heard Him? _____

7. Which words tell that Joseph and Mary worried about Jesus?

   _____

8. In which words did Jesus answer the question His mother asked Him?

   _____

9. What was His Father's house?

   _____

On the blank lines write the word from below that you think of as you read each sentence.

1. He was the Son of Mary and Joseph. _____

2. Jesus' parents went to this city every year. _____

3. It lasted seven days. _____

4. Jesus' parents looked for Him for this number of days. _____

5. Jesus was sitting in the midst of them. _____

6. She found Jesus. _____

7. Jesus had to be about His business. _____

8. Mary, Joseph, and Jesus returned there to live. _____

9. Here it was that Mary kept all Jesus' sayings. _____

10. Jesus kept this commandment when He obeyed His parents. _____

Nazareth	Jesus	teachers	Mary
heart	Jerusalem	fourth	Bethlehem
Passover	book	three	heavenly Father

The Baptism of Jesus

(Matthew 3; Mark 1)

Thinking about God's Word

1. Who came to John to be baptized?
2. How can you tell that John recognized Jesus as the Christ?
3. Why did Jesus not need to be baptized as a sign of repentance? Why, then, was He baptized?
4. How did God show Jesus as the Savior whom He had promised to send?

Working with God's Word

Answer each question.

1. From where did Jesus come to be baptized by John the Baptist?

   _____

2. How did John answer Jesus when He asked to be baptized?

   _____

3. What reason did Jesus give John for being baptized by him?

   _____

4. How was each person of the Trinity shown at this Baptism?

   _____

On the blank lines write words from below.

1. He came from Galilee to the Jordan.

   _____

2. He preached in the desert._____

3. He descended like a dove.

   _____

4. He said, "I need to be baptized by You." _____

5. He said, "Let it be so now."

   _____

6. He is the Father's beloved Son.

   _____

7. Who wrote the first book of the New Testament? _____

Holy Spirit	God the Father
John	Matthew
John the Baptist	Jesus

The Temptation of Jesus
(Matthew 4)

Thinking about God's Word

1. Into whose power had man fallen when Adam sinned?
2. Why had Jesus come into the world?
3. Why did Satan want to keep Jesus from doing His work? How did the devil plan to spoil what Jesus had come to do?
4. How did the devil first try to plant the seed of doubt into Jesus, as he once had done to Adam and Eve?
5. When Satan tempted Jesus the second time, how did he try to twist God's Word to lead Jesus into sin? How had he twisted God's Word in the Garden of Eden?
6. In the third temptation, how did the devil use humankind's love for honor and possessions to lead the Savior into sin? How had he used the same kind of temptation against Adam and Eve?
7. Which words spoken three times show that Jesus knew Scripture and used it correctly against the devil?
8. What was the difference in outcome between Satan's attempt to lead Adam into sin and his attempt to lead Jesus into sin?

Working with God's Word

Answer each question.

1. Where was Jesus led after His Baptism?

   _____

2. How long did Jesus fast there?

   _____

3. In which words did the devil first tempt Jesus to sin?

   _____

4. According to Jesus' words, by what shall man really live?

   _____

5. Where did the devil take Jesus for the second temptation?

   _____

6. How did the devil tempt Jesus there?

   _____

7. In which words did Jesus answer this temptation?

   _____

8. What did the devil say in tempting Jesus the third time?

   _____

9. What was Jesus' final answer to the devil's temptations?

   _____

10. How did the holy angels show that Jesus was their Lord?

    _____

Fill in the blanks with words from below.

1. Jesus _____ 40 days and 40 nights.

2. Jesus said, "Away from Me, _____."

3. The devil asked Jesus to turn _____ to bread.

4. The devil showed Jesus all the _____ of the world.

5. Angels came and _____ Jesus.

6. Jesus was led into the wilderness by the _____.

7. The devil asked Jesus to fall down and _____ him.

8. Jesus said, "Do not put the _____ your God to the test."

9. The devil had Jesus stand on the _____ point of the temple.

10. Three times Jesus said, "It is _____."

written	kingdoms	Satan	worship
attended	Lord	fasted	Spirit
highest	stones		

Jesus Helps Peter Catch Fish

(Luke 5)

Thinking about God's Word

1. Show that the people in this story were eager to hear God's Word.
2. What do you think Jesus talked about to the people?
3. Why did Simon not seem to think it wise to go fishing again? What was it that made him willing to let down the net, nevertheless?
4. Which words show that the net had not been made to hold so great a number of fish?
5. Which words show that the two boats together had not been built large enough to hold the catch of fish that Jesus gave them?
6. How did Peter show that he knew he had seen a miracle?
7. Which words say that these disciples now gave their whole life to being followers and disciples of Jesus?
8. Why did Jesus teach and preach? What did He preach about?

Working with God's Word

Answer each question on the blank line.

1. Why do you think Jesus got on a boat to teach the people?

   _____

2. Whose ship did Jesus use?

   _____

3. What was Jesus' command to Simon after He had finished speaking?

   _____

4. Which words tell why Simon was willing to let down the net?

   _____

5. Which words tell that many fish were in the net?

   _____

6. What did Simon Peter say when he saw all the fish? _____

7. How did these disciples give themselves to Jesus from now on?

   _____

Draw a line under the correct answer to each question.

1. What is another name for the Sea of Galilee? (Red Sea—Salt Sea—Lake of Gennesaret—Dead Sea)
2. How many boats were by the sea? (1—2—3—4—5—6—0)
3. Into whose boat did Jesus enter? (John's—James'—Simon Peter's—Philip's)
4. How was the water where Jesus told the disciples to fish? (deep—shallow—muddy—warm)
5. How many fish did they catch? (none—1—a few—many)
6. What did Jesus tell Simon Peter that he would catch from now on? (fish—draughts—thieves—men)
7. How many boats were filled with fish? (1—2—3—4—5—6—none—many)

63

Jesus Changes Water to Wine
(John 2)

Thinking about God's Word

1. Why was it not hard for Jesus' followers to believe that He was a true man?

2. How did Jesus show Himself to be true God before the people at Cana?

3. What did Jesus use to turn water into wine?

4. Which words of the lesson tell why He did this miracle?

5. Who went to Jesus for help in this lesson? Why should we go to Jesus when we need help?

6. No doubt John was present at Cana when Jesus did His first miracle. How did John and the other disciples see the glory of Jesus at Cana?

7. How many gallons did each water jar hold? How many jars were there?

Working with God's Word

Answer the questions.

1. To what were Jesus and His disciples invited in Cana? _____

2. What trouble brought Mary to Jesus for His help? _____

3. How did Jesus tell Mary that He would help at the correct time?

   _____

4. Why were six water jars in the house?

   _____

5. How did the servants obey Jesus' command to fill the water jars?

   _____

6. To whom was some water taken after it had been changed to wine?

   _____

7. Which words tell where Jesus began doing miracles?_____

8. Which words tell why Jesus did this great miracle? _____

Fill in the blanks with words from below.

1. There was a wedding the city of

   _____.

2. Mary, Jesus, and His _____ were invited.

3. The people ran out of

   _____.

4. Jesus said, "My _____ is not yet come."

5. Mary told the _____ to do whatever Jesus might command.

6. There were _____ stone water jars in this home.

7. The servants filled the water jars to the

   _____.

8. By His power, Jesus turned the _____ into good wine.

servants	mother	time
six	eight	wine
Cana	miracles	brim
water	disciples	father

81

Jesus Calms the Storm
(Mark 4)

Thinking about God's Word

1. How can it be shown from this lesson that Jesus was true man?
2. Why did the disciples awaken Jesus?
3. Why did they ask Jesus for His help even though they were experienced sailors?
4. Which part of their cry showed that they were without trust and hope, even while they asked Jesus for help? Why was this wrong?
5. In which words did Jesus tell the disciples what the real reason for all their worry and fear had been?
6. How did Jesus still the storm?
7. Why did the wind and sea obey Jesus?
8. Show from this lesson that Jesus was a true God-man.
9. Who permitted this great storm to come up? Why does God let trials and temptations come to His children?

Working with God's Word

Circle T for true and F for false.

1. This lesson says: "It had been a busy day for Jesus." T F
2. This lesson says: "Jesus was tired from a hard day's work." T F
3. This lesson says: "They got into a boat and set out." T F
4. This lesson says: "As they sailed, He fell asleep." T F
5. This lesson says: "A furious squall came up." T F
6. This lesson says: "And His disciples came to Him." T F
7. This lesson says: "Lord, save us!" T F
8. This lesson says: "Why are you so afraid?" T F
9. This lesson says: "He arose and quieted the wind." T F
10. This lesson says: "Then the wind died down and it was completely calm." T F

Circle Yes or No.

1. Jesus and His disciples wanted to reach the other side of the lake. Yes No
2. As the disciples rowed, Jesus fell asleep. Yes No
3. Because Jesus slept, we know that He was true God. Yes No
4. Jesus was sleeping in the front part of the ship. Yes No
5. Jesus rested on a pillow. Yes No
6. The great storm awakened Jesus. Yes No
7. Jesus asked the disciples why they had no faith. Yes No
8. Jesus said to the sea, "Quiet! Be still!" Yes No
9. Jesus rowed the disciples safely to shore. Yes No

Jesus Heals a Man Who Was Paralyzed

(Mark 2)

Thinking about God's Word

1. Why did the four men bring their sick friend to Jesus? How did they show their faith in His power to help?
2. Which words tell what the man needed more than the healing of his body? How could Jesus know this about the man?
3. Why did the teachers think that Jesus had mocked God?
4. What do we learn from the fact that Jesus could tell their thoughts?
5. Where did Jesus prove His power?
6. Which words of the lesson show the reason why Jesus did miracles openly?

Working with God's Word

Answer each question with one word from the lesson.

1. What was the sickness that the man of this lesson had? _____

2. To which city did the Lord return? _____

3. How many men carried the sick man? _____

4. What did the men do so the man could reach Jesus? _____

5. What did Jesus call the sick man when He spoke to him? _____

6. What kind of Jewish teachers stood among the people? _____

7. Where did the sick man go after Jesus healed him? _____

8. Whom did the people glorify when they saw the miracle? _____

Draw a line under the word or phrase that makes each sentence true.

1. They brought to Him a (feverish—paralyzed—leprous) man.

2. The man was carried by (Jesus—four men—many men—two men).

3. Jesus was (outside—inside) when the man was brought to Him.

4. The first thing Jesus did for the man was to (ask his name—heal his sickness—forgive his sins).

5. (Jesus—The sick man—The teachers) said, "Who can forgive sins but God alone?"

6. Jesus called Himself (the Messiah—the Son of Man—the Just One) in this lesson.

7. The teachers spoke evil things of Jesus (to themselves—so that all could hear it—in a low voice).

8. Jesus told the sick man to take up his (blanket—couch—mattress—mat) and go home.

9. The people who saw this miracle (laughed at the scribes—told Jesus to leave their country—glorified God).

A Widow's Son and Jairus' Daughter

(Luke 7–8)

1. How did Jesus raise the widow's son to life?
2. Why was Jairus wise in going to Jesus for help?
3. What did Jesus mean when He said, "The girl is not dead, but asleep?"
4. How did Jesus show the people of Jairus' city His power over death?
5. When did Jesus prove the same power?
6. Why did Jesus' words, "Don't cry," as spoken to the widow, really have comfort and meaning for her?
7. Because of Jesus, the death of Jairus' daughter and of the widow's son really was just a short sleep that turned out with a happy ending. Why does death mean the same thing for you, too?

Working with God's Word

Answer each question.

1. What did Jesus meet as He entered Nain one day? _____

2. Why were so many people at this funeral? _____

3. How did Jesus show His great sorrow for the mother? _____

4. By which miracle did Jesus comfort the mother? _____

5. In which words did the people glorify God upon seeing the miracle?

   _____

6. Who was Jairus? _____

7. How did Jairus show his faith in Jesus?

   _____

8. What sad message did someone bring to Jairus? _____

9. Which words of Jesus caused the people to laugh at Him?

   _____

10. How did Jesus show the people His power over death? _____

Draw a line under the correct answer to each question.

1. Where did Jesus raise a young man from the dead? (Capernaum—Judea—Jerusalem—Nain—Nazareth)

2. Over what did Jesus here show His power? (food—sickness—wind and waves—death)

3. How many sons did the widow have? (1—2—3—4—0—5)

4. How was the young man being carried? (bed—stretcher—coffin—bier)

5. Over what was Jairus a ruler? (Palestine—synagogue—Judea—Galilee)

6. How old was his sick daughter? (30—12—20—5—6)

7. What did Jesus call death in this lesson? (the end of everything—damnation—sleep—heaven)

8. How did the people in Jairus' house show unbelief in Jesus? (cast him out—laughed at him—left the room—closed their ears)

9. What was given Jairus' daughter after Jesus brought her to life? (food—wine—water—rest)

Jesus Feeds More Than Five Thousand

(John 6)

Thinking about God's Word

1. What did Jesus ask Philip? How did Philip's answer show that he thought money was of first importance in getting food for hungry people?
2. How did Andrew give a hopeless answer to Jesus' question?
3. Which words of the lesson show that Jesus gave the people more things than they wanted and needed? Why could He do this?
4. In which prayer do we say, "Give us this day our daily bread"? Why do we ask for it even when we know we'll get it?

Working with God's Word

Fill in the blanks.

1. A great _____ followed Jesus.
2. Jesus went up on a _____.
3. When Jesus looked up, He saw a great _____.
4. Jesus said to _____, "Where shall we buy bread?"
5. _____ found the boy with loaves and fishes.
6. Before Jesus gave out food, He _____ God.
7. He distributed to the people as much food as they _____.
8. Twelve baskets were filled with the _____ that remained.
9. The people saw that Jesus had done a _____.

Mark the true sentences T and the false sentences F.

1. _____ Jesus crossed to the far side of the Sea of Galilee.
2. _____ A multitude followed Him in boats.
3. _____ Jesus asked Andrew, "Where shall we buy bread?"
4. _____ Philip said that eight month's wages would not be enough.
5. _____ Andrew found a boy who had a little food with him.
6. _____ The boy had two fishes and five barley loaves.
7. _____ Jesus gave each of the five thousand a loaf and a fish.
8. _____ The people ate as much as they wanted.
9. _____ Each disciple picked up 12 baskets of fragments.

68

Jesus Walks on the Water

(Mark 6; Matthew 14)

Thinking about God's Word

1. What did the multitude whom Jesus fed want to do to Him?
2. How did the disciples obey Jesus' command? How was their faith tested that night?
3. How did they show that they didn't believe that it was Jesus when they saw Him coming toward them?
4. What did Jesus say to them? How did those words show why He had come to them?
5. Why could Jesus walk on water? Why could Peter walk on water?
6. What did Peter cry out when he began to sink?
7. Which words of Jesus tell why Peter began to sink? How did Jesus show Peter that He was the merciful Son of God?

Working with God's Word

Answer each question with one word from the story.

1. What did the people want to make of Jesus? _____
2. Whom did Jesus send away? _____
3. Who went before Him to Bethsaida? _____
4. During which watch did Jesus come to His disciples? _____
5. What did the disciples think Jesus was when they saw Him? _____
6. Who also wanted to walk on the water? _____
7. With which word did Jesus tell Peter to come to Him? _____
8. How did Peter become when he saw the wind blowing? _____
9. What died down when Jesus stepped into the boat? _____

Draw a line under the correct answer to each question.

1. Whom did the people want for their king?
   (Herod—Tabors—Jesus—Philip)

2. Why did Jesus go up on a mountainside?
   (to preach—to pray—to hide—to rest)

3. Where was the boat when a storm arose?
   (a distance from land—on the other side—along the coast)

4. When did Jesus come to the disciples?
   (at four o'clock—in the afternoon—in the fourth watch—at 4:00 A.M.)

5. How did Jesus cross the sea to get to the disciples?
   (by rowing—by sailing—by swimming—by walking)

6. What did the disciples say when they saw Jesus?
   (I see a ghost—It is our Savior—It is a spirit—Save us!)

7. Who wanted to come to Jesus on the water?
   (Andrew—the disciples—John—Peter—an angel—the people)

8. What happened when Jesus climbed into the boat?
   (The disciples cried—The disciples rowed to shore—The wind died down.)

9. How did all the disciples show that they believed Jesus to be the Son of God?
   (They left Him—They worshiped Him—They bowed to Him.)

The Faith of a Canaanite Woman

(Matthew 15)

Thinking about God's Word

1. Where did the woman in this story come from?

2. Which words of the woman showed that she knew Jesus to be the promised Savior?

3. Which words show that the woman knew she didn't deserve the help she was asking of Him?

4. What made it seem that Jesus did not care to help her?

5. For what reason did the disciples ask Jesus to send her away?

6. How did Jesus say that the woman had no right to ask His help?

7. In which words did the woman answer Jesus when He said that helping her would be like throwing children's bread to dogs?

8. In which words did Jesus say why He would answer the woman's prayer?

Working with God's Word

Answer each question.

1. Who came to Jesus for help?

2. With which words did the woman tell what was wrong with her daughter?

3. Who said, "Send her away, for she keeps crying out after us"?

4. Which words say that Jesus came for the Jews first?

5. With which words did the woman worship Jesus?

6. In which words did Jesus praise this woman's faith?

7. How did Jesus answer the faithful prayer of this woman?

Draw a line under the answer that makes each sentence true.

1. The woman who came to Jesus was a (Jew—Roman—Greek—Galilean—Babylonian).

2. The woman asked for (bread—mercy—meat—alms—great riches).

3. The woman's daughter was troubled with (palsy—leprosy—demon possession—bad dreams).

4. At first Jesus answered the woman (not a word—"Go to a doctor"—"Depart from Me"—very kindly).

5. The (people—daughter—disciples—soldiers) told Jesus to send the woman away.

6. Jesus said that it was not fair to take bread from children and throw it (away—into the river—to their dogs).

7. Jesus told the woman that her (daughter's sickness—sin—faith—age) was great.

8. Her daughter was healed from that (year—day—hour).

The Ten Lepers

(Luke 17)

Thinking about God's Word

1. Where was Jesus going?
2. Why did the men want Jesus to have pity on them?
3. Why did Jesus want the men to see the priests?
4. Who came back to praise God?
5. What did Jesus mean when He said, "Where are the other nine?"
6. Why was the leper healed?

Working with God's Word

Fill in the blank with a word from the story.

1. Jesus traveled along the border between _____ and Galilee.

2. _____ men with leprosy met Him.

3. They called, "Jesus, _____, have a pity on us!"

4. Jesus told them to show themselves to the _____.

5. One of the men came back and _____ God in a loud voice.

6. Jesus asked, "Were not all ten _____?"

7. "Where are the other _____?"

8. Jesus said to the Samaritan, "_____ and go; your faith has made you well."

Write who made these statements. Use the words Jesus, 10 men, *or* Samaritan.

1. "Were not all ten cleansed?"

   _____

2. "Rise and go; your faith has made you well." _____

3. "Jesus, Master, have pity on us."

   _____

4. "Was no one found to return and give praise to God except this foreigner?"

   _____

5. "Where are the other nine?"

   _____

6. "Go, show yourselves to the priests."

   _____

71

Jesus Blesses the Children
(Matthew 18–19)

Thinking about God's Word

1. What did the disciples ask Jesus?
2. With which direct words did Jesus tell them that if they didn't change, they wouldn't get into the kingdom of heaven?
3. How did Jesus warn the disciples that they were not to look lightly upon the child who stood in their midst nor to offend such a little believer?
4. In which words did Jesus tell the disciples that they were to lead little children to Him rather than to keep them away?
5. Who did Jesus say is the greatest in His kingdom?
6. Why must little children simply trust their parents for everything they need? With which words did Jesus tell the disciples that in order to be in His kingdom they must be toward Him as little children are toward parents?

Working with God's Word

Answer each question.

1. To whom is Jesus a particular friend?

   _____

2. Who came to Jesus to ask Him a question? _____

3. Whom did Jesus call the greatest in the kingdom of heaven? _____

4. Whom do people welcome when they welcome a child in Jesus' name?

   _____

5. Why were the children brought to Jesus?

   _____

6. Which words tell that the disciples scolded those who brought them?

   _____

7. In which words did Jesus say that He wanted children to come to Him?

   _____

8. With which act did Jesus give a sign of His love for children?

   _____

Draw a line under the correct answer to each question.

1. Who came to Jesus to ask Him a question?
   (parents—disciples—children—scribes)

2. What did they wish to know of Jesus?
   (Who Jesus' best friend was—If He loved children—Who would be greatest in the kingdom of heaven)

3. How can a person become as a little child?
   (by not studying too much—by trusting altogether in Jesus—by not sinning)

4. Who is the greatest in the kingdom of heaven?
   (the poorest—the smallest—the humblest—the wisest)

5. When is a child not a child of God?
   (when the child does not go to church every Sunday—when the child becomes older—when the child does not believe)

6. Why were the children brought to Jesus?
   (for Him to heal them—for Him to teach them—for them to pray for them)

7. How did Jesus feel when He saw what the disciples did?
   (He wept—He was not pleased—He was pleased)

8. How did Jesus show His love for the little ones?
   (He gave them presents—He kissed them—He preached to them—He blessed them)

72

The Transfiguration

(Matthew 17)

Thinking about God's Word

1. What did Jesus look like in His transfiguration?
2. Who appeared with Jesus?
3. Which disciples went with Jesus up the mountain?
4. What did Peter want to do for Jesus?
5. What did the voice from the cloud say?
6. Why were the disciples afraid?
7. Why did Jesus tell them not to tell anyone what they had seen?

Working with God's Word

Write T for true or F for false.

1. Jesus took Peter, James, and Matthew with Him to the mountain.

2. Jesus was transfigured before them.

3. Elijah and Isaiah appeared, talking with Jesus.

4. The men were talking about Jesus' departure.

5. The disciples were sleepy.

6. Peter offered to build three shelters.

7. God's voice came from a fire.

8. The disciples were terrified of the voice.

Fill in the blanks with words from the bottom.

After _____ days Jesus took _____, _____, and John up a mountain. He was _____ before them. Two men, _____ and _____, appeared with Jesus. Peter offered to build _____ for the three. A voice came from a _____ saying Jesus was God's _____. _____ told the disciples not to tell what they had seen.

Moses	two
Peter	cloud
Jesus	six
John	transfigured
Elijah	Son
James	shelters

73

Zacchaeus

(Luke 19)

Thinking about God's Word

1. Why didn't Zacchaeus go home when he couldn't see Jesus because of the crowd?
2. How do we know that Jesus was looking for Zacchaeus when He came to the tree?
3. Do Jesus' words to Zacchaeus tell all people that there is no time to waste in taking Jesus as their Savior?
4. Why did some people mutter?
5. Was Jesus the guest of a sinner? Give a reason. Why did He go there?
6. Show how Zacchaeus' life was changed after he was found by Jesus and received Him as his Savior.
7. How did those who muttered show that they did not understand why Jesus had come to them?
8. In which words did Jesus give the reason for His coming into the world.

Working with God's Word

Fill in the blanks of these sentences.

1. Jesus passed through _____.
2. A man named Zacchaeus was a chief _____.
3. Zacchaeus was a _____ man.
4. He climbed into a _____ tree to see Jesus.
5. The people _____ when they saw Jesus being kind to him.
6. Zacchaeus showed that he was sorry for his sins by returning _____ times as much goods as he had gotten dishonestly.
7. He also gave _____ of his possessions to the poor.
8. Jesus said, "Today _____ has come to this house."
9. Jesus came to save what was _____.

Draw a line under the word that makes each sentence true.

1. Zacchaeus was (the least—the oldest—the chief) tax collector.
2. Zacchaeus was very (old—kind—poor—small).
3. He lived in (Jerusalem—Jairus—Jericho—Jordan).
4. The people (shouted—muttered—rejoiced) when Jesus went into Zacchaeus' home.
5. Zacchaeus offered to give (all—half—most—one third) of his possessions to the poor.
6. If he had stolen two dollars from a man, he would return (6—2—4—10—8—20) dollars to him.
7. Zacchaeus climbed a (maple—sycamore—fig—pine—apple) tree to see Jesus.

The Lost Sheep and the Lost Coin
(Luke 15)

Thinking about God's Word

1. Who was gathering around to hear Jesus?
2. Why do you think Jesus told parables?
3. Who is meant by the lost sheep of which Jesus spoke?
4. When does a sinner cause joy in heaven?
5. What is "that which was lost" called in this parable?
6. Were you ever a lost sheep? When? How did Jesus become your Shepherd?

Working with God's Word

Answer each question correctly with words from the story.

1. Whom did the teachers and Pharisees mutter about? _____

2. How many sheep were in the flock?

   _____

3. How many sheep were lost?

   _____

4. Who went to look for the sheep?

   _____

5. Who is like the lost sheep?

   _____

6. Who looks for a lost sinner?

   _____

7. Where is there much joy when a sinner repents?

   _____

Draw a line through each sentence that is not true. Write it correctly on the blank line that follows it.

1. God wants only believers to be saved.

   _____

2. Jesus told the parable of the lost sheep.

   _____

3. Jesus welcomed sinners and ate with them. _____

4. A good shepherd will rather lose one sheep than leave 99.

   _____

5. There is joy in heaven when a sinner repents. _____

6. Some persons need no forgiveness.

   _____

7. The teachers and Pharisees did not know they were lost sheep.

   _____

8. The Son of Man is come to save that which was lost. _____

The Lost Son

(Luke 15)

Thinking about God's Word

1. What was the share of the estate the younger son got from his father?
2. What did the younger son do with his inheritance after he received it?
3. Find the words in which the son planned to say that he had sinned greatly and no longer deserved his father's love. Which words show that he had become humble?
4. How can you tell that he was truly sorry for what he had done?
5. How did he confess his sin? How did he admit that he did not deserve forgiveness?
6. How did the father show that he had never stopped loving his son and that he had already forgiven him? What did the father show by taking back his son as a member of his family?
7. What did the father mean when he said, "For this son of mine was dead and is alive again"?
8. Did the father like the son's bad deeds? How did he show that he loved him just the same? How did the father's never-ending love help the son?
9. Does God love the sins we do? What can this parable mean to our lives?

Working with God's Word

Answer each question.

1. Who told this parable?

   _____

2. For what did the younger son ask his father?

   _____

3. How did the son spend his goods?

   _____

4. Why did the son feed pigs?

   _____

5. What kind of food would the son gladly have eaten?

   _____

6. How can you tell that the father had been waiting for his son?

   _____

7. Of whom is the father of this lesson a true picture?

   _____

8. Of whom does the prodigal son remind you? _____

Draw a circle around Yes or No.

1. Did the younger son ask for his portion of the possessions?   Yes   No

2. Were there three sons in this family?   Yes   No

3. Did the prodigal son waste his money?   Yes   No

4. Did the son herd sheep during the famine?   Yes   No

5. Did the prodigal son know that he had sinned?   Yes   No

6. Does knowing that you have sinned bring forgiveness?   Yes   No

7. Did the father meet his son in a far country?   Yes   No

8. Was the prodigal son sorry for his sins?   Yes   No

76

The Foolish Rich Man
(Luke 12)

Thinking about God's Word

1. What is an abundance of possessions?
2. What did the rich man want to do?
3. What does "eat, drink, and be merry" mean?
4. What was going to happen to the rich man?
5. What does Jesus say will happen to people who seek His kingdom?
6. What does Jesus say not to worry about?

Working with God's Word

Answer each question with one word.

1. What did Jesus tell His disciples to be on guard against?

2. What produced a good crop for the rich man? _____

3. What did the rich man want to do with his grain and goods?

4. What did God call the rich man?

5. What did God say would happen to the rich man that night?

6. What did Jesus tell His disciples not to worry about?_____

Cross out the false words. Rewrite the sentences to make them true.

1. Jesus said, "Be on your guard against all kinds of corruption."

   _____

2. "The Foolish Rich Man" is a proverb.

   _____

3. Jesus told this parable to the children.

   _____

4. God told the rich man that he would die that weekend.

   _____

5. Jesus told His disciples they should worry about their lives.

   _____

6. Jesus said that people should seek His kingdom when they want.

   _____

77

The Pharisees and the Tax Collector
(Luke 18)

Thinking about God's Word

1. To whom did Jesus speak this parable? What did they think of themselves? What did they think of others?
2. How did the Pharisee show that he thought himself righteous when he spoke his prayer?
3. How did the Pharisee show in the words of his prayer that he despised others?
4. In which words did the Pharisee try to tell God of his good deeds instead of his sins? Why did he not ask for forgiveness of sins?
5. In whose wisdom, goodness, and righteousness did the tax collector put his trust?
6. What did the tax collector confess himself to be before God?
7. How did his actions show that he did not consider himself worthy to come to God?
8. What was the only thing he asked of God?
9. Read the Pharisee's "prayer" carefully. For what did he ask God?

Working with God's Word

Answer each question correctly on the blank line.

1. Which is the only way to heaven?

   _____

2. How do some people wish to enter heaven? _____

3. To whom did Jesus speak this parable?

   _____

4. Where did two men go to pray?

   _____

5. Who were the two men?

   _____

6. For what did the Pharisee thank God?

   _____

7. What was the tax collector's prayer?

   _____

8. Who trusted in himself to gain heaven?

   _____

9. Who trusted in God's mercy for salvation?

   _____

10. Who went to his house with his sins forgiven? _____

Draw a line under the word or phrase that makes each sentence true.

1. The Bible tells (two ways—many ways—one way) to be saved.
2. We (can—cannot—sometimes can) be saved by our own deeds.
3. Jesus told this parable to people who (loved—looked down on—hated) others.
4. (One—Two—Three—Four) men went up into the temple to pray.
5. The (publican—Pharisee) thanked God that he was not like others.
6. The Pharisee fasted (once—twice—three times) a week.
7. The tax collector said he was a (Pharisee—child of God—sinner—son of Abraham).
8. The tax collector went down to his house (justified—condemned—lost).

78

The Good Samaritan

(Luke 10)

Thinking about God's Word

1. What two questions did the expert in the law wish to have answered?
2. What happened to the man who was going from Jerusalem to Jericho? Which words tell that the wounded man had only a small chance to live?
3. Who came down that road?
4. Which words say that the Levite also passed the dying man without helping him?
5. Name five ways in which the Samaritan helped the man. Was that being a neighbor to the wounded man?
6. What did Jesus ask the expert in the law at the end of His parable?
7. How did the expert in the law himself now answer the question he had asked Jesus?
8. How did Jesus tell the him to be a neighbor?

Working with God's Word

Fill in the blanks.

1. Jesus told this parable to an _____.

2. A man went down from Jerusalem to _____.

3. Robbers _____ his clothes.

4. A priest passed by on the _____ side when he saw him.

5. A _____ also looked on him and passed by.

6. A Samaritan had _____ on him.

7. He poured oil and _____ into his wounds.

8. He brought the wounded man to an _____.

9. The Samaritan said to the host, "_____ after him."

10. Jesus said to the expert in the law, "Go and do _____."

If a sentence is true, mark it T; if false, mark it F.

1. _____ While going to Jerusalem, a man fell into the hands of robbers.

2. _____ The Samaritan was stripped of his clothes and was left half dead.

3. _____ The priest and the Levite were true friends in need.

4. _____ The wounded man was the Good Samaritan.

5. _____ Jesus told this parable to teach the meaning of being a neighbor.

6. _____ A person who loves God truly will love his or her neighbor, too.

The Triumphal Entry

(Matthew 21)

Thinking about God's Word

1. Why did Jesus send two disciples ahead to Bethphage? How was He going to use the animals?

2. Horses were used by soldiers and kings for warlike purposes. Donkeys were used in the everyday life of the people for moving people and things from place to place. How did Jesus show that He was coming to Jerusalem for a peaceful purpose?

3. Which prophecy was fulfilled when Jesus entered Jerusalem? What here is meant by the "daughter of Zion"? Who was the King who came to her?

4. What did the crowd do to honor Jesus as their King?

5. What did the people shout?

Working with God's Word

Fill the blanks with the correct words.

1. Jesus and His disciples were on their way to _____.

2. The disciples went to a city on the Mount of _____.

3. Only _____ of Jesus' disciples were sent to find the donkey.

4. The disciples found the donkey in the city of _____.

5. The disciples placed their _____ on the donkey as a saddle.

6. The people cried, "_____ to the Son of David!"

7. Some honored Jesus by _____ tree branches on the road.

8. Others spread their _____ on the road.

Draw a line under the correct answer to each question.

1. Toward which city were Jesus and His disciples going? (Capernaum—Bethlehem—Jerusalem—Jericho)

2. Which sad part of Jesus' life was soon to begin? (flight—preaching—suffering—ascension)

3. In which village did the disciples find the donkey for Jesus? (Jerusalem—Bethphage—Bethany—Nazareth)

4. How many disciples did Jesus send? (12—11—1—2—6)

5. Which animal was found tied with the donkey? (colt—horse—sheep—watch dog)

6. Who spoke the words, "Say to the daughter of Zion"? (the Lord—Moses—a prophet—the disciples)

7. Who rode on the donkey? (Jesus—the daughter of Zion—the disciples)

8. What name did the multitude give to Jesus? (Hosanna—Son of David—Rabbi—Savior)

9. What did Jesus show Himself to be in this lesson? (King—Savior—mighty—rich—kind)

The Anointing
(Mark 14; John 12)

Thinking about God's Word

1. In what city did the anointing take place?
2. Who served at the dinner for Jesus?
3. Who was reclining at the table with Jesus?
4. What did Mary do with the perfume?
5. Why did the people present rebuke Mary?
6. Why did Jesus tell them to leave her alone?
7. What did Jesus say would be done in memory of Mary?

Working with God's Word

Fill in the blanks with a word from below.

1. Jesus arrived in Bethany _____ days before Passover.
2. A _____ was given in Jesus' honor.
3. Mary poured _____ on Jesus' feet.
4. She wiped His feet with her _____.
5. Some said, "Why this _____ of perfume?"
6. Jesus said, "The poor you will _____ have with you."
7. The perfume was to prepare for Jesus' _____.
8. _____ betrayed Jesus.

dinner	use	always
hair	Judas	six
five	perfume	waste
burial		

Working with God's Word

Match the following by drawing lines.

1. Jesus went to   a. in Jesus' honor.
2. A dinner was given   b. anointed Jesus' feet.
3. Martha   c. hair.
4. Mary   d. expensive.
5. The perfume was   e. Bethany
6. Jesus' feet were wiped with   f. went to betray Jesus.
7. Judas   g. served at the table.

The Last Judgment

(Matthew 25)

Thinking about God's Word

1. Will this world ever come to an end? According to this parable, who will sit on the throne of the Kingdom of Glory when the time comes?
2. Who will be gathered before Him?
3. To whom will He give His kingdom? Why do they deserve to inherit the Kingdom?
4. In which words will the righteous say that their righteousness is undeserved and not their own?
5. Find the words in which the King, Jesus, says that when Christians, in faith, do good works, He counts the deeds as though they had been done to Him.
6. Whom will the King condemn into eternal fire? In Jesus' own words, why do they deserve this punishment?
7. In which words will the cursed say that the punishment is unfair?
8. How does the King tell those who are condemned that their own disobedience earned this punishment?
9. Where will the wicked then go?
10. Where will the righteous be taken?

Working with God's Word

Answer each question on the blank line below it.

1. Who will sit upon the throne of His glory at the Last Judgment?

   _____

2. Who will be gathered before Him?

   _____

3. Who will stand at the King's left hand?

   _____

4. Who shall come with the Son of Man on Judgment Day?

   _____

5. To whom shall the King first speak?

   _____

6. Of which kindnesses will the King speak to all before Him?

   _____

7. To whom will the King say, "Depart from Me, you who are cursed"?

   _____

8. Why will some be condemned to eternal fire?

   _____

Fill in the blanks of the following sentences with words from below.

1. When the Son of Man comes on Judgment Day, all the holy _____ shall come with Him.

2. All the _____ will be gathered before Him.

3. First, the King shall speak to those at His _____ hand.

4. Whatever they have done to the least of His _____, they have done to Him.

5. Afterward, the King shall speak to those on His _____ hand.

6. They must depart into eternal _____.

7. The _____ and his angels will be with the wicked.

8. Those on the left will go into _____ punishment.

9. But the righteous will go into _____ eternal.

right	brothers	nations	left
eternal	life	devil	angels
priests	fire		

82

The Lord's Supper
(Luke 22)

Thinking about God's Word

1. Which great Jewish festival was drawing near at this time?
2. What were some of the preparations necessary according to Exodus 12:3–6?
3. Whom did Jesus send to prepare the Passover?
4. How did Jesus tell His disciples that this would be the last Passover?
5. Which words show that Judas had become unfaithful before he went to the chief priests?
6. As they were eating, what did Jesus give to His disciples? What did He tell them to do with it? What did He say it was? For whom did Jesus say it was given? In whose memory were they to take it and eat it?
7. What did Jesus tell the disciples to do with the wine that was in the cup?

Working with God's Word

On the blank lines tell of whom the following things are true.

1. Who told the disciples that the Son of Man would be crucified?

   _____

2. Who entered Judas Iscariot?

   _____

3. Who went to the chief priests to betray Jesus? _____

4. Who gave Judas 30 silver coins?

   _____

5. Who went with Peter to prepare the Passover? _____

6. Who sat down with Jesus for the Passover meal? _____

7. Who took bread and broke it?

   _____

8. Who said, "Take and eat; this is My body"? _____

9. Who said, "What are you willing to give me if I hand Him over to you?"

   _____

Draw a line under the words that make the following sentences true.

1. Judas went to the chief priests because (he had been asked—he wanted to go there—he had to go there).
2. The chief priests promised to give Judas (10 shekels of silver—gold—30 silver coins—great riches).
3. Jesus sent (James and John—Peter and John—Peter and James) to prepare the Passover.
4. At the meal there were (10—11—12—13—9—15) people in all.
5. Jesus said that He desired to eat this Passover with the disciples before He (ascended—did more miracles—suffered—went to Galilee).
6. In the Lord's Supper Jesus gives us (bread and wine only—His true body and blood only—His body and blood with the bread and wine).
7. We keep the Lord's Supper to remind us of (Jesus' birth—the children of Israel in the wilderness—Jesus' first miracle at Cana—Jesus' suffering and death).

Jesus in Gethsemane

(Matthew 26; Luke 22)

Thinking about God's Word

1. Who led the way to the Mount of Olives?
2. How did Jesus warn His disciples about what they would all do that night?
3. How did Peter set himself up as better and more faithful than the rest?
4. Find the words in which Jesus warned Peter.
5. Which words tell the change that the disciples saw coming over Jesus? Which words of Jesus tell of His great sorrow?
6. Whom did Jesus take with Him to Gethsemane?
7. What was the "cup" of which Jesus spoke to His Father?
8. How often did Jesus go to pray alone? With which words did He declare that He wanted God's will to be done?
9. How many times did Jesus come to the three disciples who were to watch with Him? What did He find them doing each time? With which words did He admonish them the first time?

Working with God's Word

Answer each question correctly with one word.

1. Who said that he would never fall away from Jesus? _____
2. How often would Peter disown Jesus that night? _____
3. Who, besides Peter and John, went to Gethsemane with Jesus?

   _____

4. What did Jesus ask the heavenly Father to take from Him? _____
5. Which part of each disciple was very willing to help Jesus? _____
6. Which part of each disciple was weak?

   _____

7. How many times did Jesus go off to pray? _____
8. Who came from heaven to strengthen Jesus? _____
9. As what were the great drops of sweat which fell to the ground?

   _____

If a sentence is true, write T; if it is false, write F.

1. _____ Jesus said that all the disciples would fall away that night.
2. _____ Peter trusted in himself not to disown Jesus.
3. _____ Jesus said that Peter would disown Him before the rooster would crow.
4. _____ Three of the disciples went into Gethsemane with Jesus.
5. _____ Simon Peter watched with Jesus in Gethsemane.
6. _____ Jesus prayed three times in the garden.
7. _____ Jesus suffered greatly in the garden because soldiers were hurting Him.
8. _____ While Jesus suffered greatly, the three disciples slept.
9. _____ An angel strengthened Jesus.

Jesus Is Betrayed and Arrested

(Matthew 26; John 18)

Thinking about God's Word

1. Who came with Judas to help in capturing Jesus?

2. By which words did Jesus freely give Himself up to the mob?

3. How did Jesus show that if it were not His will they would never be able to take Him?

4. How did Judas prove himself a hypocrite when he greeted and kissed Jesus?

5. How did Peter try to save the situation? Why was this foolish as well as wrong? By which words did Jesus teach that "the sword" (earthly force and power) has no place in God's plan for saving people from sin?

6. How did Jesus point out to Peter that there was a way of getting help from His Father if it were needed or wished for?

Working with God's Word

Match the following by drawing lines to join the parts that make a true sentence.

1. Judas came
2. Jesus said to them,
3. They drew back
4. Judas said,
5. The Savior said to Judas,
6. The men seized Jesus
7. Simon Peter
8. The high priest's servant

Working with God's Word

On the blank lines tell of whom the following things are true.

1. He came with a large crowd to take Jesus. _____

2. He said, "the one I kiss, is the man." _____

3. He said, "Who is it you want?" _____

4. They said, "Jesus of Nazareth." _____

5. He said, "Greetings, Rabbi!" _____

6. He drew the sword. _____

7. His ear was cut off. _____

8. He could send more than 60,000 angels to help Jesus. _____

9. They deserted Jesus and fled. _____

a. and arrested Him.
b. alone.
c. denied Jesus and fled.
d. with a crowd of people.
e. "Greetings, Rabbi!"
f. "Depart from Me!"
g. "Who is it you want?"
h. touched his ear and healed him.
i. and fell to the ground.
j. and worshiped Him.
k. "Are you betraying the Son of Man with a kiss?"
l. had a sword.
m. had his right ear cut off.

Jesus before the Sanhedrin

(Matthew 26; John 18)

Thinking about God's Word

1. How can you see clearly from this lesson that the chief priests, the elders, and the council didn't want to give Jesus a fair trial but had made up their minds to put Him to death even before they had questioned Him? Why did Jesus' trial *have* to be an unfair one?

2. In which words did Caiaphas ask Jesus if he were the promised Messiah? What did Jesus answer?

3. From what you yourself have learned of Jesus' life, prove with five or six sentences that Jesus was the Christ, the Son of God.

4. Why didn't Caiaphas believe Jesus when He said, "It is as you say."

5. What was the sin of blasphemy of which Jesus was said to be guilty? Was He guilty?

6. If Jesus had used His almighty power, tell how He could have done the following:

   a. Come free from the ropes that bound Him

   b. Escaped from those who had taken Him to Caiaphas

   c. Proved to the council that He was God's Son

   d. Kept the men that held Him from mocking Him and spitting at Him

Working with God's Word

Answer each question on the line.

1. Who was Caiaphas?

2. Who were assembled with Caiaphas?

3. About which things did the high priest ask Jesus?

4. Who struck Jesus?

5. Why did the Sanhedrin seek evidence against Jesus?

6. What did Caiaphas tell Jesus to tell him by the living God?

7. What did the high priest say of Jesus' answer to his question?

8. With which words did all the men of the Sanhedrin condemn Jesus?

9. In which words did the soldiers mock Jesus after blindfolding Him?

Draw a line under the correct answer to each question.

1. To whom was Jesus led by the crowd?
   (Peter—Pontius Pilate—Caiaphas—Nicodemus)

2. Concerning what did the high priest ask Jesus?
   (hands and feet—disciples and teaching—mother and brethren)

3. To whom had Jesus spoken openly?
   (the world—believers only—all except Jews)

4. Who struck Jesus?
   (high priest—high priest's servant—officer—Annas)

5. Why did the Sanhedrin seek false witness?
   (to jail Jesus—to hurt Jesus' disciples—to put Jesus to death)

6. Who asked Jesus to take an oath?
   (a Roman officer—the high priest—Annas—Pontius Pilate)

7. Did Jesus ever take an oath?
   (no—yes—the Bible doesn't tell—every day)

8. How did Jesus answer Caiaphas when he asked if Jesus was the Son of God?
   (He said nothing—He said, "Yes I am"—He said, "Ask the others")

9. Why was Jesus condemned to death by the Sanhedrin?
   (He had not obeyed Caesar—He called Himself Christ—He would not answer)

10. How did the men who held Jesus speak of Him?
    (very highly—They said only good things—blasphemously—kindly)

86

Peter Disowns Jesus; Judas Dies

(Matthew 26–27; Luke 22; John 18)

Thinking about God's Word

1. To deny means that a person does not want to admit or confess something. What did Peter first deny? Why was that a sin?
2. To deny a person means to disown him or not want to know him. In which words did Peter deny Jesus? Why was that a sin?
3. What was the third denial? What sins did Peter add to that of denial?
4. How did Jesus call Peter to repentance? Which words tell Peter's great sorrow over his sin?
5. Which words speak of the sorrow that Judas showed when he saw that Jesus was condemned?
6. What did the priests say to Judas?
7. How did Judas let unbelief rob him of life?

Working with God's Word

Fill in the blanks correctly.

1. Peter followed Jesus to the high priest's _____.

2. Peter stood with the servants and officers to see the _____.

3. The _____ that kept the door said Peter was a disciple.

4. Peter _____ that he was not a disciple.

5. Peter denied _____ times.

6. The Lord turned and _____ at Peter.

7. Judas repented and brought the _____ silver coins to the priests.

8. Judas said he had betrayed _____ blood.

9. Finally, Judas went and _____ himself.

Draw a line under the correct answer to each question.

1. To which place had Peter followed Jesus?
   (Galilee—temple—Herod's palace—high priest's palace)

2. What was the work of the girl who said Peter was a disciple of Jesus?
   (building fire—serving the soldiers—keeping the door—serving meals)

3. How many times did Peter deny that he knew Jesus?
   (once—twice—three times)

4. How could it be told that Peter was from Galilee?
   (by his clothing—by his accent—by his face—by his age)

5. What sin did Peter add the third time he denied Christ?
   (adultery—coveting—cursing and swearing—suicide)

6. How was Peter reminded of Jesus' warning?
   (by a word—by a look—by a girl—by a sword)

7. How did Peter show his repentance?
   (He wept—He went to the priests—He left Jesus—He went home)

8. How did Judas show sorrow for his sin?
   (He cried—He went to Jesus—He gave back the silver—He bought a field)

9. With what sin did all the sins of Judas end?
   (adultery—coveting—cursing—suicide—swearing)

87

Jesus before Pilate
(Matthew 27; John 18)

Thinking about God's Word

1. What charge did the Sanhedrin bring against Jesus to make Him guilty of death? Knowing that Pontius Pilate would not put Jesus to death for such a reason, how did the people let their hatred of Jesus change the charge? Why was this a serious charge before the Roman governor?
2. By which words did Jesus make Pilate curious about His kingdom? How did Jesus answer the question as to whether He is a king?
3. In which words did Jesus tell Pilate why He had come into the world?
4. In which words did Pilate declare Jesus guiltless? How did he in the same breath treat Jesus as one who deserved punishment? Was that just? Why?
5. How did the people show that they wanted Jesus to be put to death?
6. What unfair treatment did Pilate let the soldiers give Jesus even when He knew that Jesus was without fault?
7. How did the chief priests and officers show only blind hatred in their hearts for Jesus?
8. Since Pilate declared Jesus to be innocent, why did he not set Him free? How did he try to "wash his hands" of Jesus' blood? Who asked that the punishment for this day's evil deeds come upon them? Actually, who paid for the sins of Pilate and Jesus' accusers?

Working with God's Word

Answer each question with Yes or No.

1. Did the Sanhedrin deliver Jesus to Caiaphas, the governor?

   _____

2. Did the Sanhedrin call Jesus guilty because He had been subverting the nation? _____

3. Did Pilate ask Jesus, "Are You the King of the Jews?" _____

4. Did Pilate say, "I have found many faults in this man"? _____

5. Did Pilate want to release Jesus?

   _____

6. Did the priests, rulers, and people want to release Jesus?

   _____

7. Did Pilate have Jesus flogged?

   _____

8. Did the people want Pilate to crucify Jesus? _____

Draw a line under the words that make each sentence true.

1. Pilate was the (high priest—governor—king).

2. The people accused Jesus of calling Himself (Caesar—God—a king—Governor).

3. Pilate asked Jesus if He were a (God—king—Christian—Roman).

4. Jesus (was—wasn't) a king.

5. Pilate soon found out that Jesus (was guilty—was true God—was innocent—was the Savior of the world).

6. The crown that Jesus wore was made of (thorns—gold—purple—reeds).

7. When Pilate brought Jesus forth, he said, ("Crucify Him!"—"Flog Him!"—"Here is the Man!"—"Scourge Him!").

8. Pilate washed his hands to show that (Jesus was innocent—he was innocent—the Jews were innocent).

9. At last Pilate said that Jesus should be (put into prison—crucified—set free—sent to Rome).

88

Jesus Is Crucified
(Luke 23; John 19)

Thinking about God's Word

1. How did the soldiers carry out the will of the Jewish leaders by order of the governor?

2. With which prayer did Jesus ask forgiveness for those who had brought Him to His death? In what way does this prayer also include you?

3. How do we know that even in His great agony Jesus thought of the welfare of His mother? Who was to take care of her from now on?

4. Which prayer to Jesus shows that one of the criminals repented in his dying hour? What certain promise did Jesus give him?

5. What did Jesus cry out at the ninth hour? Which words show that this may have been the time of His greatest suffering? Because of whose sins had God forsaken Him?

Working with God's Word

Fill the blanks.

1. Jesus carried His own

   _____ when He went to be

   crucified.

2. He went forth to a place called

   _____.

3. Two _____ were crucified

   with Jesus.

4. One criminal said, "Aren't You the

   _____? Save Yourself and

   us!"

5. Darkness came over the land at the

   _____ hour.

Circle Yes or No.

1. A soldier carried Jesus' body.

   Yes   No

2. Jesus' mother was there when He was

   on the cross.   Yes   No

3. Jesus asked God to bring revenge upon

   His enemies.   Yes   No

4. Two criminals were crucified with

   Jesus.   Yes   No

5. The darkness over the land began at

   the third hour.   Yes   No

6. Jesus asked Peter to care for his mother, Mary.   Yes   No

89

Jesus Dies and Is Buried

(Matthew 27; Luke 23; John 19)

Thinking about God's Word

1. What was Jesus given to drink?
2. What did Jesus say after He drank?
3. What did Jesus say before He died?
4. Why were Jesus' legs not broken? See Numbers 9:12.
5. How did the piercing of Jesus' side fulfill a prophecy of the Old Testament? See Zechariah 12:10.
6. How did one member of the council show honor to Jesus' body? How did another man show his love for Jesus openly?
7. How did the very fact that they were anointing Jesus show that these friends had not understood what Jesus had spoken of in Luke 18:31–34?
8. After burying His body, how did the friends of Jesus make His grave secure? How did God use the enemies of Jesus to make the grave still more secure?
9. The chief priests and Pharisees did not believe Jesus would rise. Why then did they want His grave guarded?

Working with God's Word

Answer the questions correctly on the blank lines below.

1. Why did the Jewish leaders want the legs broken of those who had been crucified? _____

2. Why were Jesus' legs not broken?
   _____

3. How did the soldiers make sure that Jesus was dead? _____

4. Who asked for the body of Jesus?
   _____

5. How did Nicodemus show his love for Jesus? _____

6. Which woman saw where Jesus was laid?
   _____

7. What did the women do on the Sabbath day? _____

8. Who met with Pilate the next day?
   _____

9. Why did the Jewish leaders want Jesus' tomb made secure? _____

10. How did Jesus' enemies make the tomb secure? _____

Write T if the sentence is true; write F if the sentence is false.

1. _____ Nicodemus asked that the legs of the crucified men be broken.
2. _____ The soldiers broke the two criminals' legs.
3. _____ Jesus' legs were pierced with a spear.
4. _____ Joseph of Arimathea was a follower of Jesus.
5. _____ Nicodemus brought a mixture of myrrh and aloes.
6. _____ Jesus' 11 disciples buried Him.
7. _____ The friends of Jesus rested on the Sabbath day.
8. _____ Jesus' enemies knew that He had said, "After three days I will rise again."
9. _____ Pilate gave the disciples a guard.
10. _____ Jesus' disciples sealed the stone.

The Resurrection of Christ

(Matthew 28; Mark 16)

Thinking about God's Word

1. On what day had Jesus died? During which full day was He dead? How can you tell that it was now the third day?
2. Why did the women go to the tomb? What question did they ask on the way?
3. Who had already rolled the stone away? Who became alarmed when they saw him?
4. To whom did Mary Magdalene run when she saw that the stone was rolled away? What did she think?
5. With what glorious message did the angel explain the empty grave?
6. To whom were the women to tell the glad news first? Whose name was especially mentioned?
7. Where would the disciples see Jesus with their own eyes?
8. Read the entire message of the angel. Note how many things he said in those few words. What are they? Which is the most important to you?

Working with God's Word

Answer each question with one word.

1. Who was the mother of James?

   _____

2. On what day of the week did the women reach the tomb?

   _____

3. Who rolled back the stone for the women? _____

4. Of whom is it said that they shook and became like dead men?

   _____

5. Who said, "They have taken the Lord out of the tomb"? _____

6. Who was the disciple whom Jesus loved? _____

7. Who said, "He has risen! He is not here"? _____

9. Who entered the tomb and saw a young man? _____

10. Where would Jesus show Himself to the disciples and Peter?

    _____

Answer each question correctly by putting a circle around Yes or No.

1. Did the women go to the grave on the Sabbath day?   Yes   No
2. Is Sunday the first day of the week?   Yes   No
3. Did the angel roll the stone away to let Jesus out?   Yes   No
4. Did Salome tell Peter and John that the tomb was empty?   Yes   No
5. Did all the women enter Jesus' tomb?   Yes   No
6. Was an angel in the tomb?   Yes   No
7. Did Jesus arise from the dead on Sunday?   Yes   No
8. Did the disciples steal Jesus' body?   Yes   No
9. Was Jesus in the grave for three days?   Yes   No
10. Did Jesus break the chains of death for us?   Yes   No

The First Appearances of the Risen Lord

(Matthew 28; John 20)

Thinking about God's Word

1. Who were the first people to whom the risen Lord appeared?

2. Why did Mary not recognize Jesus at first? What did she say when Jesus said her name?

3. What message did Jesus tell her to give the disciples?

4. What did Jesus call the disciples? What did this show about His love for them, even though they had forsaken Him three days ago?

5. How did the words "go" and "tell" show that Jesus was thinking of others who were fearful and needed comfort?

Working with God's Word

Each sentence below has one mistake in it. Draw a line through the wrong word and write the correct one in its place.

1. Mary stood near the tomb, sleeping.

2. Peter asked her whom she was seeking.

3. Mary thought that Jesus was an angel.

4. Rabboni means "Messiah."

5. Mary Magdalene told the women that she had seen the Lord.

6. Jesus met the women and said to them, "All glory!"

7. They held Jesus by the feet, and they kissed Him.

8. The guards told the chief officers all the things that had happened.

9. The soldiers were paid to say, "His enemies came during the night and stole Him away."

Draw a line under the words that make each sentence true.

1. The woman who came to Jesus' grave was (Martha—Jesus' mother—Mary Magdalene).

2. She thought that Jesus was a (soldier—counselor—gardener—minister).

3. Jesus said to her, ("Greetings!"—"Rabboni"—"Mary"—"Don't cry").

4. Mary said to Jesus, ("Greetings"—"Rabboni"—"Mary"—"Don't cry").

5. Mary Magdalene told (Jesus' mother—the disciples—the women—the chief priests) that she had seen Jesus.

6. The women held Jesus by the (feet—hands—arms—side).

7. The (disciples—guards—women—Pharisees) told the chief priests what had been done at the grave.

8. The soldiers were given (promises—punishment—money) to lie.

92

Christ Appears to His Disciples
(John 20; Matthew 28)

Thinking about God's Word

1. When did Jesus appear to His disciples? What was the disciples' reaction?
2. With which words did Jesus greet the disciples?
3. How did Jesus now let the doubting disciples convince themselves that He was really the same Jesus who had lived among them before His death? Read the words that show that the disciples now believed.
4. By what sign did Jesus show that He was now giving them the Holy Spirit? What important power did He give them?
5. With which words did Jesus now remind them that He was no longer the humble Servant, but the exalted Lord of heaven and earth?
6. As the risen Lord who would live forever, Jesus gave His servants a last command. What are the words of this important commission?
7. From the Great Commission, write the words that tell
   a. that the One giving the command is the Lord of heaven and earth;
   b. that the disciples were to go to others instead of waiting for them to come to them;
   c. who was to go;
   d. what they were to do;
   e. whom they were to teach and baptize;
   f. in whose name they were to baptize;
   g. what things they should teach;
   h. that people should be taught to observe or do what Christ commanded.

Working with God's Word

Fill in the blanks.

1. The doors were locked for fear of the _____.
2. When Jesus appeared, the disciples thought they saw a _____.
3. Jesus said unto them, "Why are you _____?"
4. He _____ them His hands and His feet.
5. The _____ were overjoyed when they saw the Lord.
6. Jesus _____ on His disciples.
7. Then the 11 _____ went into Galilee.
8. There they worshiped Him; but some _____.
9. Jesus said, "Go and make disciples of all _____."
10. Jesus said, "I am with you _____."

116

Fill in the blanks with words from below.

1. Jesus came to His disciples on the _____ day of the week.

2. Jesus stood among them and said, "_____ be with you."

3. The disciples thought that they saw a _____.

4. Jesus said, "A ghost does not have _____."

5. Jesus showed His disciples His hands and His _____.

6. Jesus said, "If you forgive anyone his _____, they are forgiven."

7. Then the _____ disciples went into Galilee.

8. When the disciples saw the Lord, they _____ Him.

9. Jesus said, "Go and make disciples of all _____."

first	body and blood	flesh and bones
Peace	feet	twelve
ghost	first	worshiped
sins	eleven	nations

The Ascension

(Acts 1)

Thinking about God's Word

1. Why did Jesus show Himself on earth after He had proved His power over death and the devil?

2. In which words did Jesus promise a special gift to His disciples? Where were they to wait until He sent it? Which words tell what the gift would be?

3. Where did Jesus lead His disciples after He had spoken to them? Why did He lift up His hands?

4. In what way was Jesus no longer to be with His disciples? In what way would He remain with them all the time?

5. How did God's messengers announce that Jesus will come again?

6. How do you know the disciples understood the words of the angels?

Working with God's Word

Answer each question Yes or No.

1. Is Jesus' resurrection absolutely true? _____

2. Did Jesus' disciples see Him alive for 50 days "after His suffering"? _____

3. Did Jesus say, "Wait for the gift My Father promised"? _____

4. Did John baptize with water? _____

5. Did Jesus ask the disciples to stay in Bethany? _____

6. Did Jesus and His disciples go to Bethany? _____

7. Did Jesus bless His disciples before He left them? _____

8. Were two men standing by the disciples as Jesus ascended? _____

9. Will Jesus come again in the same way as He ascended? _____

10. Did the disciples worship the angels before returning? _____

Cross out the sentences that are not true. Write them correctly on the blanks.

1. Jesus lived on earth 40 years after His resurrection. _____

2. The disciples were to leave Jerusalem and start preaching immediately.

_____

3. Jesus ascended into heaven at Bethany.

_____

4. Twelve disciples saw Jesus ascend.

_____

5. An angel stood by the disciples as Jesus ascended. _____

6. Jesus blessed His disciples before He left them. _____

7. Jesus now sits at the right hand of God.

_____

8. We will see Jesus some day.

_____

9. The disciples were sad when they returned to Jerusalem.

_____

The Holy Spirit Comes at Pentecost

(Acts 2)

Thinking about God's Word

1. By what sign did the Holy Spirit enter the room in which the disciples were gathered? What showed that the Spirit had entered the disciples?

2. By what miracle did the disciples show that the Holy Spirit had come upon them? Which words tell that the Holy Spirit told them what to say?

3. Which words of the people give us an idea of what things the disciples preached?

4. What did some in the crowd say of this Pentecost miracle? Why?

5. Tell how Peter began the work of "catching men" which Jesus had foretold of him in Matthew 4:18–19.

6. Read Peter's words. According to Peter, what did Jesus' miracles, His suffering and death, and His resurrection prove Him to be? Why could Peter be so sure of Jesus' power to do miracles, of His death, and of His resurrection?

7. How can you tell that Peter was now filled with the Holy Spirit?

8. Which words show that the people were sorry for what they had done? How did Peter tell them they could obtain forgiveness for all their sins? How did the Lord bless the words spoken by Peter?

Thinking about God's Word

On the blank lines tell of whom the following things are true.

1. They were all together in one place.

   _____

2. He gave the disciples power to speak with other tongues. _____

3. God-fearing people were there from every nation under heaven.

   _____

4. They were all amazed and bewildered.

   _____

5. They said, "They have had too much wine." _____

6. He said, "Men of Israel, listen to this."

   _____

7. He was accredited by God by miracles.

   _____

8. He told the people to repent and to be baptized. _____

9. People must repent and be baptized in His name. _____

Draw a line under the words that make each sentence true.

1. The disciples began to speak in other (voices—fires—tongues).

2. (The Holy Spirit—The Son—The Father) came upon the disciples.

3. (James—Peter—Israel—John) preached to the multitude.

4. Jesus had been accredited by God by (the Jews—everyone—miracles).

5. (Peter—The Holy Spirit—The disciples) opened the hearts of the people so that they repented.

6. About (30,000—300,000—3,000—300) people became Christians that day.

The Crippled Beggar Is Healed

(Acts 3)

Thinking about God's Word

1. Why was the crippled man at the gate of the temple? Why was the temple the best place to which people could be brought if they needed mercy from other people?
2. What did the lame man expect of Peter and John?
3. What did the lame man receive which was better than silver and gold?
4. How did the man show his thankfulness for what he had received?
5. From which words can you see the reason for performing this miracle at the time and in the place it was done?
6. How did Peter take this opportunity to preach repentance to the people?
7. To whom did Peter and John give all glory for the miracles? In which words did Peter tell the people what they had done? How did he offer the love and forgiveness of Jesus to all? Who were the ones who received the forgiveness?

Working with God's Word

Answer each question with one word.

1. Who went to the temple with John?

    _____

2. At what time was the crippled man healed? _____

3. Who took the crippled man by the hand and helped him up?

    _____

4. Whom did the crippled man praise?

    _____

5. Who saw the crippled man walking?

    _____

6. Who spoke to the people?

    _____

Draw a line under the words that make each sentence true.

1. The disciple with Peter was named (Andrew—John—James—Philip).
2. The crippled man expected (clothing—food—healing—money).
3. The likeliest people to help a beggar are the (rich—crippled—nonbelievers—Christians).
4. Peter and John gave the man (silver and gold—a good home—healing—his youth) in the name of Jesus.
5. Peter took him by (the left hand—the right hand—both hands) and helped him up.
6. The man could walk again (in the same hour—the next day—immediately—soon afterward).
7. The man was healed by (Peter's—John's —God's—Peter and John's) power.
8. The first place that the healed man went was (to his wife—to Jesus—home—to the temple courts).
9. The people who saw this miracle were brought to Christ by (the miracle—the crippled man—God's Word—the crowd).
10. After Peter's sermon the number of believers grew to about (3,000—4,000—5,000—10,000).

96

Stephen

(Acts 6–8)

Thinking about God's Word

1. According to Acts 6:1–5 what was Stephen's work?

2. Which words tell why Stephen could do miracles?

3. Who stirred up the people against Stephen? What accusations did they bring against him?

4. Read Stephen's reply to the accusations against him. How had the fathers of the Jews been stiff-necked? Who was the Righteous One who had been betrayed and murdered?

5. Which words of the lesson tell that Stephen's words upset his accusers?

6. Why could Stephen look into heaven? Whom could he see there?

7. How did the false witnesses kill Stephen because he spoke the truth for Jesus' sake? With which simple prayer did Stephen place his soul into the hands of his Lord? How did Stephen's last prayer show his enemies that he had a real interest in their souls' salvation?

8. Whose name is especially mentioned as being pleased with Stephen's death?

Working with God's Word

Fill in the blanks.

1. Stephen did great _____ among the people.

2. Certain members of the _____ argued with Stephen.

3. These people produced false _____ against Stephen.

4. They said Stephen never stopped _____ against the temple.

5. The council saw that Stephen's face was the face of an _____.

6. Stephen said the people were murderers of the _____ One.

7. The men were _____ and gnashed their teeth at him.

8. They rushed at him and _____ him out of the city.

9. Then they _____ Stephen.

10. _____ gave approval to his death.

Write a T or F in the blank.

1. _____ Stephen was a man full of God's grace and power.

2. _____ Stephen did great wonders among the people.

3. _____ Those who argued with Stephen found it simple to disprove what he taught.

4. _____ The men who testified against Stephen were honest men.

5. _____ When Stephen spoke to the Sanhedrin, his face shone like the sun.

6. _____ A young man named Saul tried to save Stephen from the hands of the mob.

7. _____ When Stephen died, he asked God to bring revenge upon his murderers.

Philip and the Ethiopian

(Acts 8)

Thinking about God's Word

1. Where did the angel tell Philip to go?
2. Whom did Philip meet on the way?
3. What was the man doing?
4. What did the Spirit tell Philip to do?
5. What did Philip ask the man?
6. What did Philip do with water?
7. What happened to Philip?
8. What did the man do?

Working with God's Word

Fill in the blanks with words from the story.

1. An angel of the Lord spoke to _____.

2. He went south on the road that went from Jerusalem to _____.

3. On his way, he met an _____ eunuch.

4. The Ethiopian had gone to _____ to worship.

5. The Ethiopian was reading the book of _____.

6. He asked _____ to come sit with him.

7. Philip told the Ethiopian the good news about _____.

8. Philip _____ the Ethiopian with water.

9. The _____ of the Lord took Philip away.

10. The Ethiopian went on his way _____.

Put these events in order from 1–7.

____ Philip baptized the Ethiopian.

____ The Ethiopian was in his chariot reading.

____ Philip sat with the man.

____ Philip met an Ethiopian while he was walking.

____ Philip disappeared.

____ The Ethiopian left rejoicing.

____ Philip explained the good news about Jesus.

Saul's Conversion

(Acts 9)

Thinking about God's Word

1. How did Saul try to get rid of those who believed Christ's doctrine and taught it to others?
2. What happened to Saul on the way to Damascus?
3. Whose voice was it that spoke to Saul? What did He say?
4. Why did Jesus say that Saul was persecuting Him when he had been persecuting the disciples?
5. Which words show that Saul's heart was changed toward Jesus?
6. With which words did Ananias assure Saul that his sins were forgiven? How did Saul show that he had accepted the Lord Jesus as His Savior?
7. How did Saul now show love instead of hate toward the disciples? Whose name did he preach instead of blaspheme? What did Saul testify of Jesus?

Working with God's Word

Of whom are the following things true?

1. He breathed out murderous threats against the disciples. _____

2. He gave Saul letters to Damascus. _____

3. He said, "Saul, Saul, why do you persecute Me?" _____

4. He said, "Who are You, Lord?" _____

5. He came from Tarsus. _____

6. He lived in Damascus. _____

7. He visited Saul at the Lord's command. _____

8. He received his sight and was baptized at Damascus. _____

9. They watched the gates of Damascus day and night. _____

10. They lowered Saul in a basket through an opening in the wall. _____

Draw a line under the word that answers each question correctly.

1. Where did Saul wish to go to persecute Christians?
   (Samaria—Tarsus—Jerusalem—Damascus—Capernaum)

2. What did he plan to do with the Christians he found?
   (kill them—hang them—send them home—take them to Jerusalem)

3. Who spoke to Saul when he fell to the ground?
   (the soldiers—Jesus—Ananias—the high priest)

4. What happened to Saul when he got up?
   (He was blind—There was no one—It was night—He closed his eyes)

5. What was the name of the disciple who lived at Damascus?
   (Judas—Peter—Ananias—Tarsus—John—Andrew)

6. In whose house did Saul stay?
   (Judas'—Peter's—Ananias'—Tarsus'—John's—Andrew's)

7. To whom was Saul to bear Jesus' name and His Gospel?
   (poor people—Samaritans—Gentiles—disciples)

8. When the disciple spoke to Saul, what did he call him?
   (you sinner—poor sinner—Paul—Brother Saul—sir)

9. How long was Saul in Damascus?
   (3 weeks—several days—3 days—many years)]

10. In whose name did Saul speak when he returned to Jerusalem?
    (the disciples'—Ananias'—the high priest's—the Lord's)

Peter Is Freed from Prison

(Acts 12)

Thinking about God's Word

1. Why was King Herod arresting Christians?
2. Who was put in prison?
3. How many guarded the prisoner?
4. Who appeared in the cell?
5. What happened to Peter's chains?
6. Where did Peter go?
7. Who answered the door at Mary's house?
8. Did the people believe Peter was at the door?
9. What did Peter tell the people?

Working with God's Word

Fill in the blanks with words from below.

King _____ arrested some who belonged to the church. He put _____ in prison. Peter would go on trial after the _____. The members of the _____ were praying for Peter. One night an _____ appeared in Peter's cell. The chains fell off of Peter's _____. Peter followed the _____ out of prison. Then he went to _____ house. The people did not believe it was _____. When they saw him, they were _____. _____ described how the Lord had brought him out of prison.

church   angel   Passover
Martha's   legs   Peter
astonished   Mary's   Herod
wrists

Answer each question.

1. Who was king?

   _____

2. Why was the king arresting Christians?

   _____

3. Where was Peter put?

   _____

4. How many soldiers guarded Peter?

   _____

5. When would Peter go on trial?

   _____

6. What did the angel tell Peter to do?

   _____

7. What did Peter think he was seeing?

   _____

8. Why did Peter go to Mary's house?

   _____

9. What did the believers in Mary's house think was wrong with the servant?

   _____

10. What did Peter describe?

   _____

100

Paul's Shipwreck

(Acts 27–28)

Thinking about God's Word

1. Why was Paul at sea?
2. What was the weather like?
3. Why was the cargo thrown overboard?
4. What did Paul tell the hungry men?
5. Who told Paul not to be afraid?
6. Where did they decide to run the ship aground?
7. What were the soldiers going to do with the prisoners?
8. Who wanted to spare Paul's life?
9. How many people died in the shipwreck?
10. How did the people of Malta treat the prisoners?

Put these events in order from 1–7.

_____ Everyone reached land safely.

_____ The men gave up hope of being saved.

_____ Paul and other prisoners set sail for Italy.

_____ The centurion helped Paul stay safe.

_____ An angel stood beside Paul.

_____ The people of Malta welcomed the men.

_____ A wind of hurricane force hit the ship.

Working with God's Word

Fill in the blanks with words from below.

1. Paul was sailing to _____.

2. A _____ swept down from the island.

3. The ship took a violent _____ from the storm.

4. Neither sun nor _____ appeared for many days.

5. The men gave up _____ of being saved.

6. An _____ appeared to Paul.

7. The angel said all would be _____.

8. A _____ helped spare Paul's life.

9. The prisoners landed on _____.

10. The islanders were _____.

angel	storm	wind
Malta	moon	centurion
Italy	saved	kind
stars	battering	hope

126

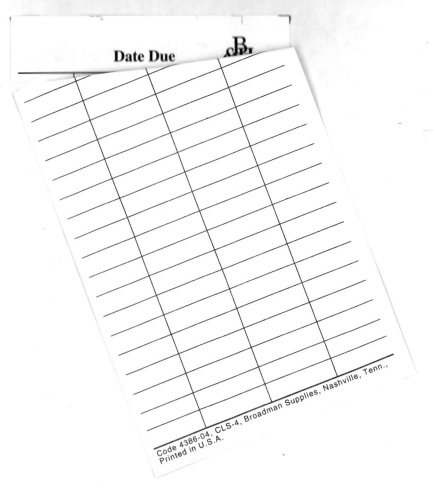

Date Due